SCHOLASTIC
LITERACY
PLACE®

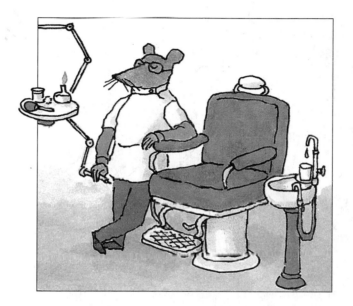

Acknowledgments and credits appear on pages 390–391, which constitutes an extension of this copyright page.

ISBN 0-439-06150-4

3 4 5 6 7 8 9 10   09   07 06 05 04 03 02 01 00

TABLE OF CONTENTS

What's New?

THEME
We learn about our world through new experiences.

UNIT 1

TABLE OF CONTENTS

Big Plans

THEME
Making and using plans can help you solve problems.

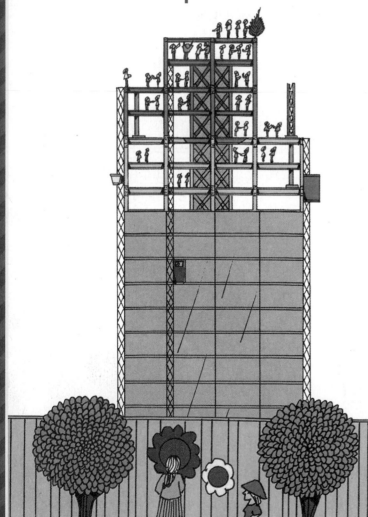

UNIT 2

TABLE OF CONTENTS

THEME
Teams work best when they use each member's strengths to get the job done.

What's New?

What's New?

THEME

We learn about our world through new experiences.

UNIT 1

Welcome to

LITERACY PLACE

Wilderness School

We learn about our world through new experiences.

Gila monsters meet you at the airport

AWARD
WINNER

by Marjorie Weinman Sharmat
illustrated by Byron Barton

« 1 »

I live at 165 East 95th Street, New York City,
and I'm going to stay here forever.

My mother and father are moving. Out West.

They say I have to go, too.
They say I can't stay here forever.

Out West nobody plays baseball because they're
too busy chasing buffaloes.

And there's cactus everywhere you look.
But if you don't look, you have to stand up
just as soon as you sit down.

Out West it takes fifteen minutes just to say hello.
Like this: H-O-W-W-W-D-Y, P-A-A-A-R-D-N-E-R.

Out West I'll look silly all the time. I'll have to wear
chaps and spurs and a bandanna and a hat so big that
nobody can find me underneath it. And I'll have to ride
a horse to school every day and I don't know how.

Out West everybody grows up to be a sheriff.
I want to be a subway driver.

My best friend is Seymour, and we like to eat
salami sandwiches together.

Out West I probably won't have any friends,
but if I do, they'll be named Tex or Slim,
and we'll eat chili and beans for breakfast. And lunch.
And dinner. While I miss Seymour and salami.

« 2 »

I'm on my way. Out West. It's cool in the airplane.

The desert is so hot you can collapse, and then
the buzzards circle overhead, but no one rescues
you because it's real life and not the movies.
There are clouds out the window.
No buzzards yet.

I'm looking at a map. Before, whenever I looked
at a map, I always knew my house was on the right.
But no more.
Now I'm in the middle of that map,
and I'm going left, left. Out West.

Seymour says there are Gila monsters and
horned toads out West, and I read it in a
book so I know it's so.
But Seymour says they meet you at the airport.

We're here.

Out West.

I don't know what a Gila monster or horned toad looks like, but I don't think I see any at the airport.

I see a boy in a cowboy hat.

He looks like Seymour, but I know his name is Tex.

"Hi," I say.

"Hi," he says. "I'm moving East."

"Great!" I say.

"*Great?*" he says. "What's so great about it? Don't you know that the streets are full of gangsters? They all wear flowers in their lapels so they look honest, but they zoom around in big cars with screeching brakes. You have to jump out of their way.

"In the East it snows and blows all the time,
except for five minutes when it's spring and summer.

"And you have to live on the 50th floor. Airplanes fly
through your bedroom, and you've got to duck fast.

"They ran out of extra space in the East a long time
ago. It's so crowded people sit on top of each other
when they ride to work.

"And alligators live in the sewers. I read it in a book
so I know it's so."

Then the mother and father of the boy who looks like
Seymour but isn't grab his hand, and he goes off.
"Sometimes the alligators get out," he yells to me.
"And they wait for you at the airport."

« 4 »

It's warm, but there's a nice breeze.
We're in a taxi riding to our new house.

No horses yet.
I don't see any buffalo stampedes either.

I see a restaurant just like the one in my old
neighborhood.

I see some kids playing baseball.

I see a horse. Hey, that's a great-looking horse!
I'm going to ask my mother and father for one like it.

Here's our house.
Some kids are riding their bikes in front of it.
I hope one of them is named Slim.

Tomorrow I'm writing a long letter to Seymour.
I'll tell him I'm sending it by pony express.
Seymour will believe me.
Back East they don't know much about us Westerners.

from
The Reptile Ball

by Jacqueline K. Ogburn pictures by John O'Brien

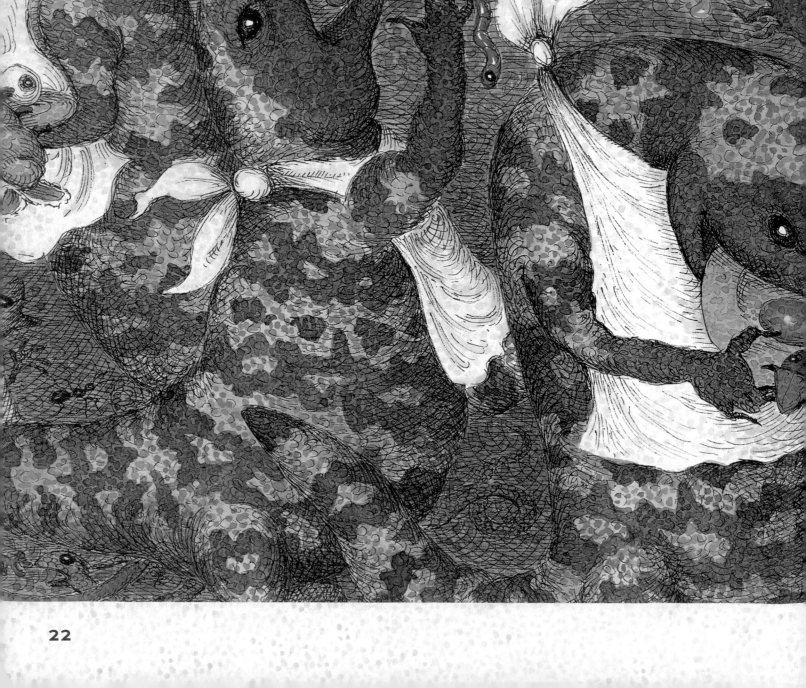

Gila Monster March

Gilas come marching, two by two.
Gilas are black and pink and blue.
   Gilas are rowdy,
   Gilas are rude.
Gilas don't dance —
They've come for the food.

Alligator Stomp

Suave Egyptian crocodiles
Crack wicked, toothy smiles,
When their cousins from the swamp
Start the Alligator Stomp.
Clomp!

Kin from Cairo and Decatur,
Both sides of the equator,
Grinning leatherbacks thomp
In the Alligator Stomp.
Clomp!

Smaller dancers have to run
From the table-smashing fun
Of the tail-swinging romp
Called the Alligator Stomp.
CLOMP!

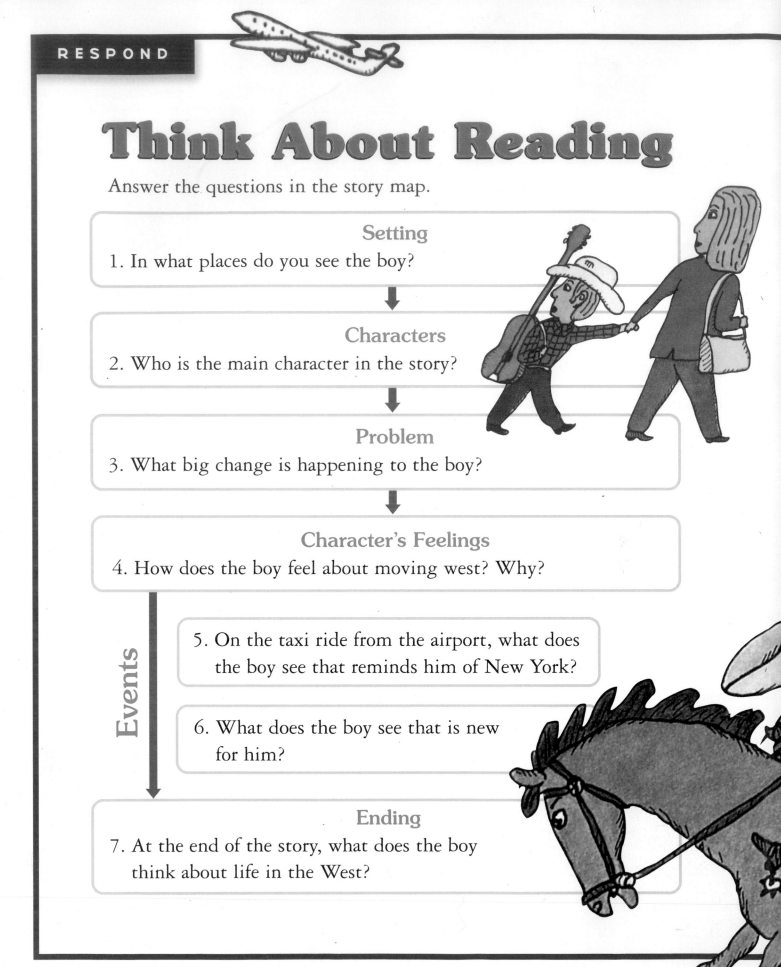

Think About Reading

Answer the questions in the story map.

Setting

1. In what places do you see the boy?

Characters

2. Who is the main character in the story?

Problem

3. What big change is happening to the boy?

Character's Feelings

4. How does the boy feel about moving west? Why?

Events

5. On the taxi ride from the airport, what does the boy see that reminds him of New York?

6. What does the boy see that is new for him?

Ending

7. At the end of the story, what does the boy think about life in the West?

Write A Postcard

Imagine you are the boy in the story. Write a postcard to Seymour. Tell him one interesting thing about your new home. It might be about a new friend or something fun you did. Be sure to include the date, a greeting, a short message, and a closing.

Literature Circle

The story and the poems are examples of humorous writing. Which descriptions, ideas, or events made you laugh? What made them funny?

Author
Marjorie Weinman Sharmat

Marjorie Weinman Sharmat always wanted to be a writer. She and a friend published a newspaper when she was only eight. Many of her books are about things that happened to her. In fact, she wrote *Gila Monsters Meet You at the Airport* after she moved from New York City to Arizona with her husband and sons. Did she meet any Gila monsters? You'll have to ask her.

More Books by
Marjorie Weinman Sharmat

- *Nate the Great*
- *Getting Something on Maggie Marmelstein*
- *Genghis Khan: A Dog Star Is Born*
- *I'm the Best*

from

RamOna

FOREVER

by **Beverly Cleary**

illustrated by **Alan Tiegreen**

AWARD WINNER

*It's an exciting time for the Quimby family!
Ramona's mother has just had a beautiful baby girl.
Visiting her mother and baby Roberta at the hospital
will be a real thrill, but Ramona is also worried. A
baby around the house could change everything.*

The day was long and lonely. Even a swimming
lesson at the park and a trip to the library did little to
make time pass. "I wonder what Roberta looks like?"
said Beezus.

"And whose room she will share when she outgrows
the bassinette?" worried Ramona.

The one happy moment in the day for the girls was a telephone call from their mother, who reported that Roberta was a beautiful, healthy little sister. She couldn't wait to bring her home, and she was proud of her daughters for being so good about staying alone. This pleased Beezus and Ramona so much they ran the vacuum cleaner and dusted, which made time pass faster until their father, looking exhausted, came home to take them out for hamburgers and a visit to the fifth Quimby.

Ramona could feel her heart pounding as she finally climbed the steps to the hospital. Visitors, some carrying flowers and the others looking careworn,

walked toward the elevators. Nurses hurried, a doctor was paged over the loudspeaker. Ramona could scarcely bear her own excitement. The rising of the elevator made her stomach feel as if it had stayed behind on the first floor. When the elevator stopped, Mr. Quimby led the way down the hall.

"Excuse me," called a nurse. Surprised, the family stopped and turned.

"Children under twelve are not allowed to visit the maternity ward," said the nurse. "Little girl, you will have to go down and wait in the lobby."

"Why is that?" asked Mr. Quimby.

"Children under twelve might have contagious diseases," explained the nurse. "We have to protect the babies."

"I'm sorry, Ramona," said Mr. Quimby. "I didn't know. I am afraid you will have to do as the nurse says."

"Does she mean I'm *germy*?" Ramona was humiliated. "I took a shower this morning and washed my hands at the Whopperburger so I would be extra clean."

"Sometimes children are coming down with something and don't know it," explained Mr. Quimby. "Now, be a big girl and go downstairs and wait for us."

Ramona's eyes filled with tears of disappointment, but she found some pleasure in riding in the elevator alone. By the time she reached the lobby, she felt worse. The nurse called her a little girl. Her father called her a big girl. What was she? A germy girl.

Ramona sat gingerly on the edge of a Naugahyde couch. If she leaned back, she might get germs on it, or it might get germs on her. She swallowed hard. Was her throat a little bit sore? She thought maybe it was, way down in back. She put her hand to her forehead the way her mother did when she thought Ramona might have a fever. Her forehead was warm, maybe too warm.

As Ramona waited, she began to itch the way she itched when she had chickenpox. Her head itched, her back itched, her legs itched. Ramona scratched. A woman sat down on the couch, looked at Ramona, got up, and moved to another couch.

Ramona felt worse. She itched more and scratched harder. She swallowed often to see how her sore throat was coming along. She peeked down the neck of her blouse to see if she might have a rash and was surprised that she did not. She sniffed from time to time to see if she had a runny nose.

Now Ramona was angry. It would serve everybody right if she came down with some horrible disease, right there in their old hospital. That would show everybody how germ free the place was. Ramona squirmed and gave that hard-to-reach place between her shoulder blades a good hard scratch. Then she scratched her head with both hands. People stopped to stare.

33

A man in a white coat, with a stethoscope hanging out of his pocket, came hurrying through the lobby, glanced at Ramona, stopped, and took a good look at her. "How do you feel?" he asked.

"Awful," she admitted. "A nurse said I was too germy to go see my mother and new sister, but I think I caught some disease right here."

"I see," said the doctor. "Open your mouth and say 'ah'."

Ramona *ahhed* until she gagged.

"Mh-hm," murmured the doctor. He looked so serious Ramona was alarmed. Then he pulled out his stethoscope and listened to her front and back, thumping as he did so. What was he hearing? Was there something wrong with her insides? Why didn't her father come?

The doctor nodded as if his worst suspicions had been confirmed. "Just as I thought," he said, pulling out his prescription pad.

Medicine, ugh. Ramona's twitching stopped. Her nose and throat felt fine. "I feel much better," she assured the doctor as she eyed that prescription pad with distrust.

34

"An acute case of siblingitis. Not at all unusual around here, but it shouldn't last long." He tore off the prescription he had written, instructed Ramona to give it to her father, and hurried on down the hall.

Ramona could not remember the name of her illness. She tried to read the doctor's scribbly cursive writing, but she could not. She could only read neat cursive, the sort her teacher wrote on the blackboard.

Itching again, she was still staring at the slip of paper when Mr. Quimby and Beezus stepped out of the elevator. "Roberta is so tiny." Beezus was radiant with joy. "And she is perfectly darling. She has a little round nose and—oh, when you see her, you'll love her."

"I'm sick." Ramona tried to sound pitiful. "I've got something awful. A doctor said so."

Beezus paid no attention. "And Roberta has brown hair—"

Mr. Quimby interrupted. "What's this all about, Ramona?"

"A doctor said I had something, some kind of *itis*, and I have to have this right away." She handed her father the prescription and scratched one shoulder. "If I don't, I might get sicker."

Mr. Quimby read the scribbly cursive, and then he did a strange thing. He lifted Ramona and gave her a big hug and a kiss, right there in the lobby. The itching stopped. Ramona felt much better. "You have acute siblingitis," explained her father. "*Itis* means inflammation."

Ramona already knew the meaning of sibling. Since her father had studied to be a teacher, brothers and sisters had become siblings to him.

"He understood you were worried and angry because you weren't allowed to see your new sibling, and prescribed attention," explained Mr. Quimby. "Now let's all go buy ice-cream cones before I fall asleep standing up."

Beezus said Roberta was too darling to be called a dumb word like sibling. Ramona felt silly, but she also felt better.

For the next three nights, Ramona took a book to the hospital and sat in the lobby, not reading, but sulking about the injustice of having to wait to see the strange new Roberta.

On the fourth day, Mr. Quimby took an hour off from the Shop-rite Market, picked up Beezus and Ramona, who were waiting in clean clothes, and drove to the hospital to bring home his wife and new daughter.

Ramona moved closer to Beezus when she saw her mother, holding a pink bundle, emerge from the elevator in a wheelchair pushed by a nurse and followed by Mr. Quimby carrying her bag. "Can't Mother walk?" she whispered.

"Of course she can walk," answered Beezus. "The hospital wants to make sure people get out without falling down and suing for a million dollars."

Mrs. Quimby waved to the girls. Roberta's face was hidden by a corner of a pink blanket, but the nurse had no time for a little girl eager to see a new baby. She pushed the wheelchair through the automatic door to the waiting car.

"*Now* can I see her?" begged Ramona when her mother and Roberta were settled in the front, and the girls had climbed into the back seat.

"Dear Heart, of course you may." Mrs. Quimby then spoke the most beautiful words Ramona had ever heard, "Oh, Ramona, how I've missed you," as she turned back the blanket.

Ramona, leaning over the front seat for her first glimpse of the new baby sister, tried to hold her breath so she wouldn't breathe germs on Roberta, who did not look at all like the picture on the cover of *A Name for Your Baby*. Her face was bright pink, almost red, and her hair,

unlike the smooth pale hair of the baby on the cover of the pamphlet, was dark and wild. Ramona did not know what to say. She did not feel that words like darling or adorable fitted this baby.

"She looks exactly like you looked when you were born," Mrs. Quimby told Ramona.

"She does?" Ramona found this hard to believe. She could not imagine that she had once looked like this red, frowning little creature.

"Well, what do you think of your new sister?" asked Mr. Quimby.

"She's so—so *little*," Ramona answered truthfully.

Roberta opened her blue gray eyes.

"Mother!" cried Ramona. "She's cross-eyed."

Mrs. Quimby laughed. "All babies look cross-eyed sometimes. They outgrow it when they learn to focus." Sure enough, Roberta's eyes straightened out for a moment and then crossed again. She worked her mouth as if she didn't know what to do with it. She made little snuffling noises and lifted one arm as if she didn't know what it was for.

"Why does her nightie have those little pockets at the ends of the sleeves?" asked Ramona. "They cover up her hands."

"They keep her from scratching herself," explained Mrs. Quimby. "She's too little to understand that fingernails scratch."

Ramona sat back and buckled her seat belt. She had once looked like Roberta. Amazing! She had once been that tiny, but she had grown, her hair had calmed down when she remembered to comb it, and she had learned to use her eyes and hands. "You know what I think?" she asked and did not wait for an answer. "I think it is hard work to be a baby." Ramona spoke as if she had discovered something unknown to the rest of the world. With her words came unexpected love and sympathy for the tiny person in her mother's arms.

"I hadn't thought of it that way," said Mrs. Quimby, "but I think you're right."

"Growing up is hard work," said Mr. Quimby as he drove away from the hospital. "Sometimes being grown-up is hard work."

"I know," said Ramona and thought some more. She thought about loose teeth, real sore throats, quarrels, misunderstandings with her teachers, longing for a bicycle her family could not afford, worrying when her parents bickered, how terrible she had felt when she hurt Beezus's feelings without meaning to, and all the long afternoons when Mrs. Kemp looked after her until her mother came from work. She had survived it all. "Isn't it funny?" she remarked as her father steered the car into their driveway.

"Isn't what funny?" asked her mother.

"That I used to be little and funny-looking and cross-eyed like Roberta," said Ramona. "And now look at me. I'm wonderful me!"

"Except when you're blunderful you," said Beezus.

Ramona did not mind when her family, except Roberta, who was too little, laughed. "Yup, wonderful, blunderful me," she said and was happy. She was winning at growing up.

POEM

from It's Raining Laughter
by Nikki Grimes

photographs by
Myles C. Pinkney

AWARD WINNER

I Am

I laugh
shout
sing
smile
whisper
hum
howl
gurgle
giggle
sigh.

I am joy.

Think About Reading

Answer the questions in the story map.

Setting
1. Where does the story take place?

Characters
2. Who are the main characters in the story?

Problem
3. Why couldn't Ramona see her new baby sister in the hospital?

Events

4. What did Ramona do as she sat in the waiting room?

5. How did the doctor help her?

Ending
6. How did Ramona's feelings about baby Roberta change at the end of the story?

7. What did Ramona think about herself at the end of the story?

Write an E-Mail Message

Ramona wants to E-mail all her friends about baby Roberta. Write an E-mail message that Ramona might send. Tell what Roberta looks like and how she acts. Be sure to describe Ramona's feeling about the new member of the Quimby family.

Literature Circle

Are there any characters who change during the story? If so, how do they change? What makes them different? Make a chart to show what you think.

Author
Beverly Cleary

Books have always been important to Beverly Cleary and her family. Her mother opened the first lending library in the town where the Clearys lived. Beverly Cleary couldn't wait to learn how to read. When she did learn, she found that the stories were very different from her own life. "I wanted to read funny stories about the sort of children I knew, and I decided that someday when I grew up I would write them."

More Books by
Beverly Cleary

- *Ramona and Her Father*
- *Henry Huggins*
- *Muggie Maggie*

WORKSHOP 1

How to

Make a Milestone Chart

Think of all the things you have learned and done since you were small. Each of these important events is a milestone in your life. These events can be shown on a milestone chart.

What is a milestone chart? A milestone chart lists important events. It shows the order in which each event happened.

the writer's age when the events happened

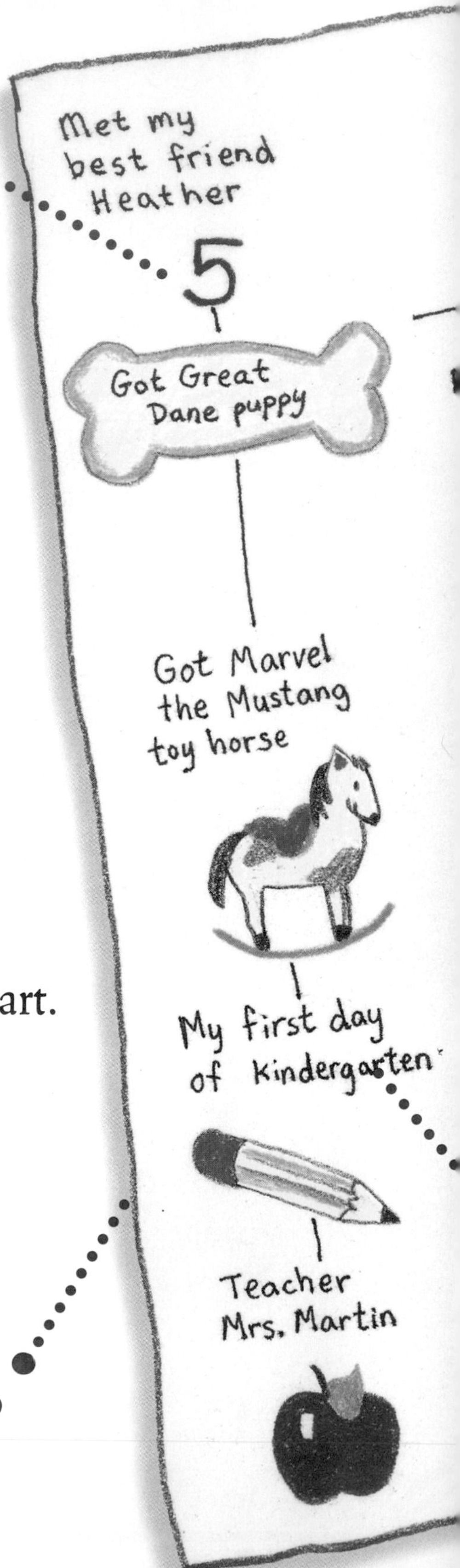
Met my best friend Heather
5
Got Great Dane puppy
Got Marvel the Mustang toy horse
My first day of Kindergarten
Teacher Mrs. Martin

chart runs from left to right

taking a fun trip

I wore a white party dress on my birthday

Teacher gave me a toy house on the last day of school

went to summer camp

6   7   8   9   10   11

Mom brought home a black and white kitten

My first bike ride

First time I wore pants to school

Won my 1st horse show ribbon

Went to Colorado to visit my Grandmother

Teacher Mrs. Cooper

Flew on airplane alone to Colorado

Got record player

Went to the Aquarium in Golden Gate Park

My first pony

learning to do something new

getting a new pet

starting school

47

1 Which Milestones?

Make a list of some important events that have happened to you. You might begin with your first day in kindergarten. Think of things you've learned, new places you've seen, and new people in your life.

Here are some ideas: a new baby, a trip, learning to do something, moving, making a friend, or special holidays or events.

TOOLS

- pencil and paper
- tape
- small pieces of paper or index cards

2 Which Was First?

Now you need to put your milestones in order. There is an easy way to do this. Write each milestone on an index card or small piece of paper. If you know the year it happened, write that on the card, too.

Spread the cards out on a table. Put them in the order they happened. Then, number the cards so you will always know their order.

3 Make the Chart

Now it's time to make your milestone chart.

- Tape two large pieces of paper together.
- Draw a line across the paper going the long way.
- Decide if you want to make your chart run from left to right or from top to bottom.
  - Begin at the top or left side of the paper. Next to the line, write your first milestone.

Tip Use your numbered index cards to write the rest of your milestones in order. You may want to illustrate some of your milestones.

4 Show It!

Display your milestone chart on the class bulletin board. Discuss your chart with your classmates. Tell which milestones were most important to you. Look at the other charts. Do you share any of the same milestones with your classmates?

If You Are Using a Computer...

Create your milestone chart on the computer using a program like HyperCard. Make a stack of cards about your life, with each card showing a different milestone.

THINK

Learning to do something new is one kind of milestone. What would you want to learn next?

Keith Jardine
Wilderness Guide ▶

from

How My Family Lives in America

by Susan Kuklin

AWARD WINNER

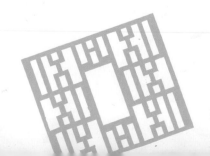

My name in America is April. I also have a Chinese name: *Chin* (ching), which means "admire" and *Lan* (lan), which means "orchid."

Both my parents are Chinese and were born in Taiwan. Taiwan is an island on the other side of the world. My papa came to New York without his parents to go to school and my mama moved here with her family. Because Julius, my older brother, and May, my older sister, and I were born in America, we are called Chinese Americans.

There are many Chinese Americans. But we do not all speak the same Chinese language. The way my family speaks Chinese is called Mandarin.

Admire

Orchid

爸爸
Father

媽媽
Mother

In Mandarin, I call my daddy *baba* (bah-bah) and my mommy *mama* (mah-mah). It sounds something like English, but when we write the words they look very different. Another thing that's different in Chinese is that words aren't made with letters. Each word has its own special marks.

During the week we go to public school, but on Saturday we go to Chinese school. There we learn how to speak and write in Chinese, like my parents learned in Taiwan. When I write English letters, I write from the left side of the page to the right. When I write in Chinese, I write from the right to the left. And I write in rows from the top of the page to the bottom. For us Chinese-American kids there are many things to remember.

52

In Chinese school we also learn a special kind of writing called calligraphy. We use a brush instead of a pen, black ink, and special paper made from stalks of rice. Our teacher shows us the right way to hold the brush.

芝
蔴
涼
麵

Cold Sesame
Noodles

My favorite part of Chinese school is snack time. Today, Mama made me cold sesame noodles, *tsu ma liang mein* (tsu mah leeang mee-en). I eat them with a fork, but most Chinese people eat their noodles with chopsticks. I'm just learning to eat with chopsticks.

Papa told us that an Italian explorer named Marco Polo discovered noodles in China a long time ago and introduced them to his country.

When Mama brought home takeout, Julius asked if a Chinese explorer discovered pizza in Italy.

Mama and Papa laughed and said, "No."

While we eat our pizza we play a game to test our wits. Papa asks us to look for letters hidden in the picture on the pizza box. Julius sees a *V* in the pizza man's shoe. May finds an *L*.

Oh, look! I can even see the Chinese letter *Ba* (bah), in the pizza man's eyebrows. *Ba* means "eight" in Chinese.

Eight

七
巧
板

Chi chiao
bang

At night when we have finished all our chores and all our homework, we play *Chi chiao bang* (chee chow bang). In America some people call it Tangram. This is a popular game in Taiwan, like checkers is in America. My grandparents and even my great-grandparents played this game. To play, you move seven different shapes to build a new shape. I like to make a pussycat. It is very difficult, but I can do it. Papa says, "Go slowly and think about a cat. After a while your mind will start to run and you will see the cat in the shapes." He's right.

There is an old Chinese saying, "The older you are the wiser you become." When I become a grown-up, I will remember to tell this to my family.

April's Cold Sesame Noodles

(1 serving)

2 ounces cooked Chinese noodles or spaghetti
1 tablespoon sesame sauce or peanut butter
1 teaspoon soy sauce
1 teaspoon chopped scallion

In a bowl mix the sesame sauce (or peanut butter) with 1 tablespoon warm water and soy sauce. Add to the cooked, cooled noodles and sprinkle scallion on top. Stir before eating.

AWARD
WINNER

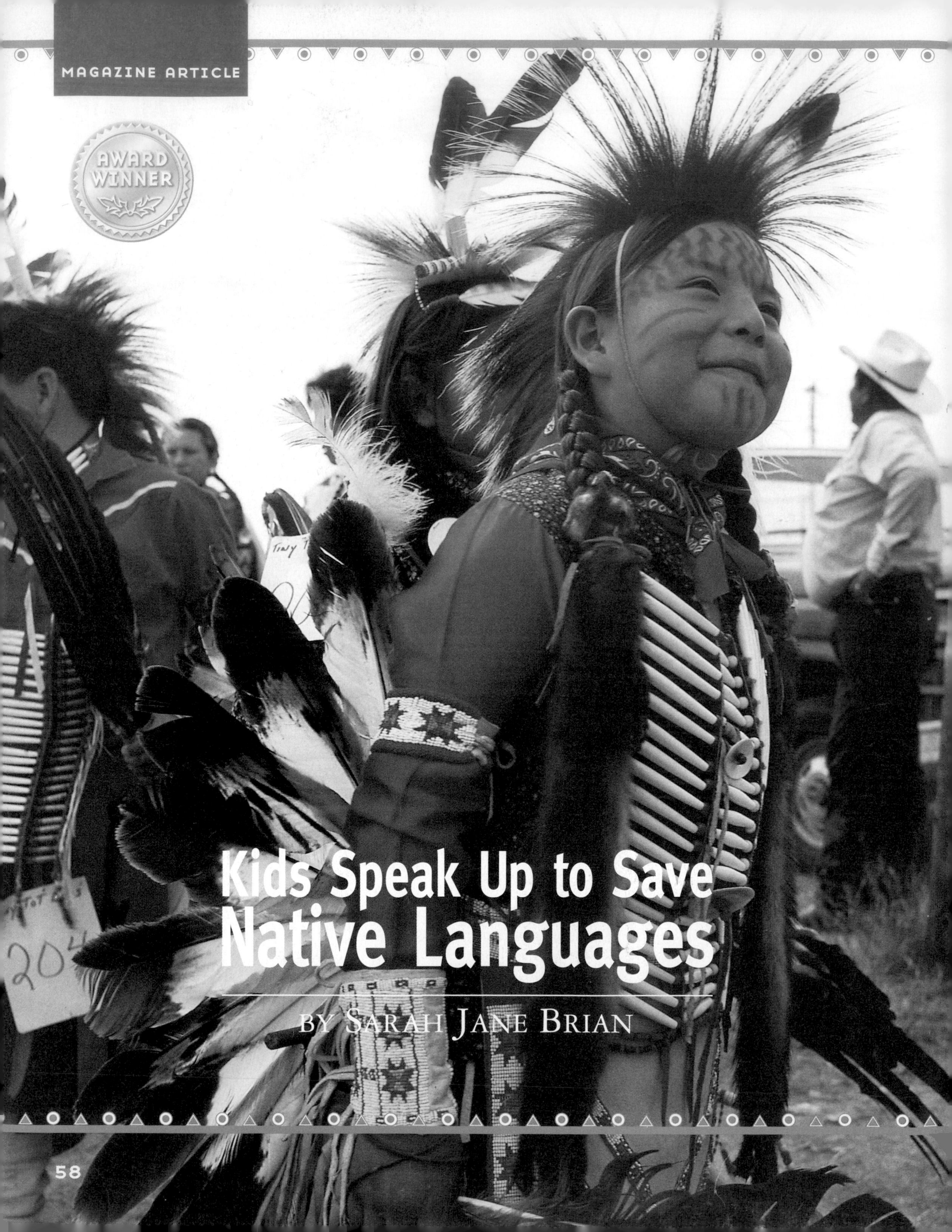

Kids Speak Up to Save
Native Languages

BY SARAH JANE BRIAN

◀ **Wearing colorful handmade costumes and dancing are two ways that Native Americans keep their traditions alive.**

"*Hey-yung*!"

That means "hello" in the Native American language of Hupa (HOOP-ah). For thousands of years, Hupa people used this language to share their thoughts, feelings, and ideas. Today, only 20 people speak Hupa well enough to hold a conversation. All of them are older members of the tribe, called elders. Most children and young adults in the tribe speak English, and know only a few Hupa words.

▲
This Cherokee storyteller passes on traditional tales to interested listeners.

Fourth grader David Drake wants to make sure his tribe's language doesn't die out. He is one of many Hupa kids who are trying to learn Hupa before it is too late. Last summer, David and his family went to a special language camp. There, they cooked and ate traditional foods, sang songs, and listened to stories in Hupa. "It was fun," David said. "During everything that we did, we learned new words in Hupa."

◀ **A young Navajo girl is learning her native language in school.**

▲ During a 4th of July powwow, or get-together, these Kiowa boys and girls learn traditional dances and stories.

Lost Languages

Hupa is not the only language that is in trouble. According to expert Dr. Clay Slate, more than 1,000 different native languages were once spoken in North America. Most of them have been forgotten. Today, there are only 206 of these languages left.

In the past, the U.S. government wanted Native Americans to give up their languages. David's great-grandmother was punished when she spoke Hupa in school. Today, that has changed. In 1990, the U.S. Congress passed a law to help protect native languages. Soon, a new law may provide money for tribes that want to save their languages.

Getting Tongues Un-tied

Navajo teacher Andrew Becenti says we must save native languages because they are important parts of Native American cultures. "If you don't have the language, and you try to teach the culture, it's like food without any salt. Something's missing. It's just flat," he said.

All across the U.S., many Native Americans are already working to preserve their languages. In some places, elders work to teach younger people. On the Navajo reservation in Tuba City, Arizona, kids can take Navajo language classes in school.

Learning to speak a new language is not easy. It can take years. But people like David and his family plan to study hard for as long as it takes. "Our language is part of our heritage. We can't just let it die off," said David's mom.

WHERE AMERICAN INDIANS LIVE

Long before Columbus arrived, nearly a million people lived in America. Columbus called them Indians. They belonged to different tribes across the land. Today nearly two million American Indian people live in the U.S. states shown on this map.

Most live in towns and cities. But many live on reservations—pieces of land that have been set aside for native tribes. The large blue areas on the map show the larger reservations. The small blue areas show smaller reservations and other places where American Indians live.

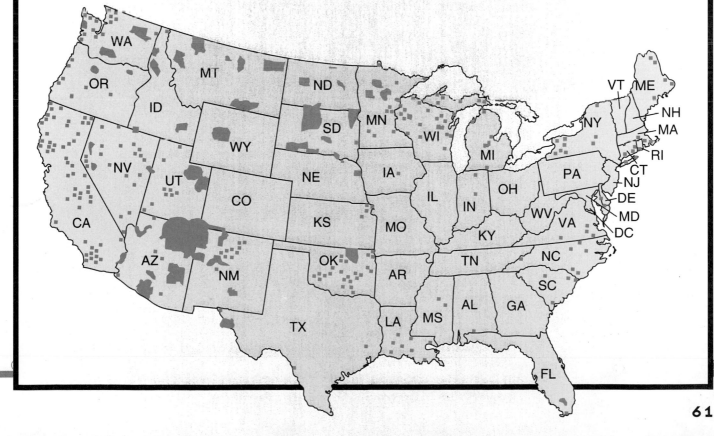

Think About Reading

Write your answers.

1. What does April do each Saturday?

2. Why do April's parents want her to learn calligraphy and to play Tangram?

3. How is April's Saturday school like your school? In what ways is it different?

4. Why do you think Susan Kuklin used photos to illustrate this story?

5. In what way does David Drake in "Kids Speak Up to Save Native Languages" remind you of April in *How My Family Lives in America*?

Write a Caption

Even a great photograph needs a caption.
Look at the photographs that Susan Kuklin
took of April. Choose three of them. Write
a caption for each one. Tell who is pictured.
In a few words, tell what is happening.

Literature Circle

Think about *How My Family Lives in
America* and "Kids Speak Up to Save
Native Languages." How are the two
articles alike? How are they different? Talk
about the kinds of information in each
article. Think about each author's purpose.
Use a Venn diagram to record your ideas.

Author
Susan Kuklin

Photographer and author
Susan Kuklin has always
been interested in art and
people's stories. After college
she acted in plays and even
taught school for a while.
Her interest in art led her to
photography. Then she put
all her interests—people,
photography, and stories—
together and began to make
nonfiction books for children.
Her goal is to help people
better understand each other.

More Books by
Susan Kuklin

- *Fighting Fires*
- *Kodomo: Children of Japan*
- *Taking My Dog to the Vet*

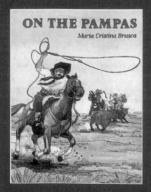

ON THE PAMPAS

by María Cristina Brusca

I grew up in Argentina, in South America. I lived with my family in the big city of Buenos Aires, but we spent our summers in the country, at my grandparents' *estancia*. One summer my parents and brother stayed in the city, so I went without them.

My grandmother met me at the station in Buenos Aires, and we had breakfast as we rode through miles and miles of the flattest land in the world—the pampas. All around us, as far as we could see, were fences, windmills, and millions of cattle grazing.

Our station, San Enrique, was at the end of the line, where the train tracks stopped. My grandfather was there to meet us in his pickup truck and take us the five miles to the estancia.

The ranch was called La Carlota, and the gates were
made of iron bars from a fort that had been on that very
spot a hundred years before. As we drove up to the gates,
we were greeted by a cloud of dust and a thundering of
hooves—it was my cousin Susanita, on her horse.

Susanita lived at the estancia all year round. She knew
everything about horses, cows, and all the other animals
that live on the pampas. Even though she was three years
younger than me, she had her own horse, La Baya.
Susanita was so tiny, she had to shimmy up La Baya's leg
to get on her back. But she rode so well that the gauchos
called her La Gauchita—"The Little Gaucho."

I didn't have a horse of my own, but old Salguero, the ranch foreman, brought me Pampita, a sweet-tempered mare, to ride. She wasn't very fast, but she certainly was my friend.

Susanita and I did everything together that summer. She was the one who showed me how to take care of the horses. We would brush their coats, trim their hooves, and braid their manes and tails.

Susanita was always ready for an adventure, no matter how scary. She used to swim in the creek holding on to La Baya's mane. At first I was afraid to follow her, but when she finally convinced me, it was a lot of fun.

I wanted to learn all the things a gaucho has to know. I wanted to ride out on the pampas every day, as Salguero did, and to wear a belt like his, with silver coins from all over the world and a buckle with my initials on it. Salguero said I'd have to begin at the beginning, and he spent hours showing Susanita and me how to use the lasso.

It was going to take a while for me to become a gaucho. The first time I lassoed a calf, it dragged me halfway across the corral. But Salguero told me that even he had been dragged plenty of times, so I kept trying, until I got pretty good at it.

Whenever the gauchos were working with the cattle, Susanita was there, and before long I was too. Sometimes the herd had to be rounded up and moved from one pasture to another. I loved galloping behind hundreds of cattle, yelling to make them run. I never got to yell like that in the city!

One day we separated the calves from the cows, to vaccinate them and brand them with "the scissors," La Carlota's mark. That was more difficult—and more

exciting, too. I tried to do what Salguero told me to, but sometimes I got lost in the middle of that sea of cattle.

At noon, everybody would sit down around one big table and eat together. I was always hungry. Grandma, Susanita's mother, and Maria the cook had been working hard all morning too. They would make soup, salad, and lamb stew or pot roast, or my favorite, *carbonada*, a thick stew made of corn and peaches.

After lunch the grown-ups took a *siesta*, but not us. We liked to stay outdoors. Some afternoons, when it was too hot to do anything else, we rode out to a eucalyptus grove that was nice and cool, and stayed there until it got dark, reading comic books or cowboy stories.

Other times we would gallop for two hours to the
general store and buy ourselves an orange soda. Then,
while we drank it, we'd look at all the saddles and bridles
we planned to have when we were grown up and rich.
Sometimes the storekeeper would take down a wonderful
gaucho belt like Salguero's, and we would admire the silver
coins and wonder where each one came from.

One day we rode far away from the house, to a field
where Susanita thought we might find *ñandú* eggs. They
are so huge, you can bake a whole cake with just one of
them. After riding around all afternoon, we found a nest,
well hidden in the tall grass, with about twenty pale-yellow
eggs as big as coconuts.

Salguero had warned us to watch out for the ñandú, and he was right! The father ñandú, who protects the nest, saw us taking an egg. He was furious and chased us out of the field.

The next day we used the ñandú egg to bake a birthday cake for my grandmother. We snuck into the kitchen while she was taking her siesta, so it would be a surprise. The cake had three layers, and in between them we put whipped cream and peaches from the trees on the ranch.

We had a wonderful party for my grandmother's birthday.
The gauchos started the fire for the *asado* early in the evening,
and soon the smell of the slowly cooking meat filled the air.

There was music, and dancing, too. We stayed up
almost all night, and I learned to dance the *zamba*, taking
little steps and hops, and twirling my handkerchief.

Most evenings were much quieter. There was just the
hum of the generator that made electricity for the house.
We liked to go out to the *mate* house, where the gauchos
spent their evenings.

We listened to them tell ghost stories and tall tales
while they sat around the fire, passing the gourd and
sipping mate through the silver straw. We didn't like the
hot, bitter tea, but we loved being frightened by their
spooky stories.

The summer was drawing to a close, and soon I would be returning to Buenos Aires. The night before I was to leave, Salguero showed me how to find the Southern Cross. The generator had been turned off, and there was only the soft sound of the peepers. We could see the horses sleeping far off in the field.

The next morning, my last at the estancia, Susanita and I got up before dawn. Pampita and the other horses were still out in the field. Salguero handed me his own horse's reins. He told me he thought I was ready to bring in the horses by myself. I wasn't sure I could do it, but Susanita encouraged me to try.

I remembered what I'd seen Salguero do. I tried to get the leading mare, with her bell, to go toward the corral, and the others would follow her. It wasn't easy. The foals were frisky and kept running away. But I stayed behind them until finally the little herd was all together, trotting in front of me.

I was so busy trying to keep the foals from running off that I didn't notice the whole household waiting in the corral with Salguero. Everyone cheered as I rode in, and before I knew it, my grandfather was helping me off the horse. "You've become quite a gaucho this summer," he said.

My grandmother held out a wonderful gaucho belt like Salguero's, with silver coins from around the world—and my initials on the buckle!

"And," she added, "there's something else every gaucho needs. Next summer, when you come back, you'll have your very own horse waiting for you!" She pointed to the leading mare's foal, the friskiest and most beautiful of them all.

Before I could say a word, the foal pranced over to me, tossing his head. I would have the whole winter to decide what to name him, and to look forward to my next summer on the pampas.

MULITA

(moo-LEE-ta)
The mulita is a kind of armadillo. It spends the day in its burrow and comes out at night to look for food, mostly spiders and insects.

LAS PAMPAS

(las POM-pas)
The pampas are the very flat, almost treeless grasslands that stretch for hundreds of miles through central Argentina and Uruguay. Ranch animals live on the pampas year round, even during the mild winter months, eating grass.

HORNERO

(or-NAIR-oh)
The hornero is a kind of oven bird. Its nest looks something like an oven and is built out of clay, usually on top of a post or pole.

REBENQUE

(ray-BAIN-kay)
A short, wide rawhide strap, used to lash cattle and horses.

LA CARLOTA'S BRAND

(la car-LOH-ta)
The brand represented two crossed fencing swords, but we called it "the scissors."

VENEZUELA
COLOMBIA
GUYANA
SURINAME
FRENCH GUIANA
ECUADOR
SOUTH AMERICA
PERÚ
BRAZIL
BOLIVIA
PARAGUAY
ARGENTINA
URUGUAY
THE PAMPAS
BUENOS AIRES
LA CARLOTA
CHILE
SOUTH PACIFIC OCEAN
SOUTH ATLANTIC OCEAN

LECHUZA

(lay-CHOO-sa)
The lechuza, or burrowing owl, makes its home in holes abandoned by armadillos or other mammals. It likes to hunt in the evening.

YEGUA MADRINA

(YAY-goo-ah mah-DREE-na)
The yegua madrina, or leading mare of a herd of horses, keeps the herd together. She generally has a bell around her neck.

ASADO
(ah-SAH-doh)
Meat, usually beef, roasted outdoors over a fire.

MATE
(MAH-tay)
Mate is a bitter, greenish tea. It is sipped through a silver straw called a bombilla *(bome-BEE-yah) from a hollow gourd that is passed around.*

FACÓN
(fah-KONE)
A gaucho knife. Gauchos used to carry them as weapons, but now they are used for ranch work.

BOLEADORAS
(boh-lay-ah-DOOR-ahs)
Gauchos used to catch ñandús and other animals with boleadoras, which they threw in such a way that the animals' legs were tangled up in them.

GAUCHO CLOTHES

RASTRA
(RAH-stra)
A gaucho belt made from a wide strip of leather decorated with silver coins, usually from different countries. Some gauchos have their initials on the buckle.

BOMBACHA
(bome-BAH-cha)
Loose gaucho pants.

ÑANDÚ
(nyon-DOO)
The ñandú, or South American ostrich, is the largest bird in the Americas. It grows to be five feet tall and to weigh about fifty pounds. Although it cannot fly, it can run very fast. The male ñandú guards the nest, hatches the eggs, and takes care of the chicks.

RECADO
(ray-KAH-doh)
The gaucho saddle, made of many layers of leather and wool, with a sheepskin on the top.

ESTANCIA
(eh-STAHN-see-ah)
A South American cattle ranch.

Keith Jardine

Wilderness Guide

River rafting is full of new experiences!

Wilderness guide Keith Jardine works for a wilderness school. But his workplace isn't an indoor classroom. Instead, he grabs a paddle, puts on a life jacket, and jumps into a rubber raft. Jardine's job is taking adults and kids on adventure trips down some of California's fastest-moving rivers. And he loves every minute of it!

PROFILE

Name: Keith Jardine

Born: Sonoma, California

Job: wilderness guide

Hobby: river rafting

First wilderness experience: exploring his own backyard

Favorite wilderness place: California's Clavey River. He even named one of his sons Klavey, spelled with a K.

Fantasy adventure trip: rafting on a wild Alaskan river

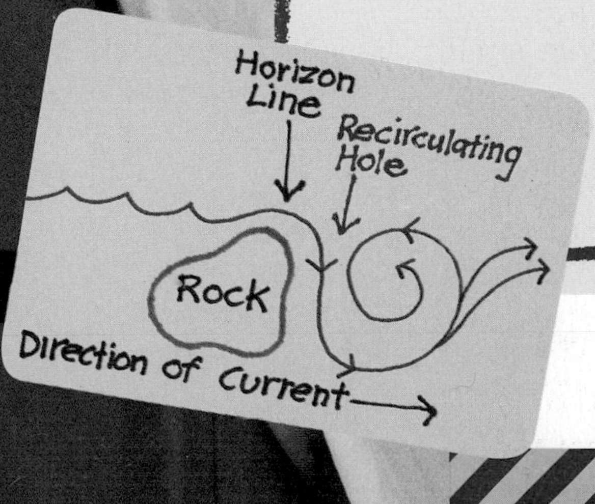

Horizon Line
Recirculating Hole
Rock
Direction of Current

ALL ABOUT
Keith Jardine

Here's how wilderness guide Keith Jardine teaches kids to meet adventure head on.

"River rafting is a lot of fun," says Keith Jardine. "But it also takes a willingness to learn. You can't just jump in a boat and float down the river."

Jardine especially likes taking kids on raft trips. He finds that they are willing to listen and learn about the wilderness experience.

"Some kids already know a lot about the wilderness," says Jardine. "They're usually the ones who come from small towns and have spent time hiking or camping. But rafting is a different experience for city kids," he explains. "For many of them, the adventure is new and even scary."

What happens when kids are nervous about rafting? "I'm there to help them out," says Jardine. If kids are afraid to get into the raft, he tells them that they don't have to go. But he always asks them to give it a try. "By the time they're down the river a half mile, their attitudes usually change. They really start to enjoy it."

Jardine feels that wilderness adventures, on and off the river, can help kids find out about themselves. "They learn that it is okay to get out in the world and explore new things."

Exploring and looking for adventure have always been a part of Keith Jardine's life. As a kid he went hiking and camping with his parents. They taught him how to get along by himself in the woods. Meeting these challenges gave Jardine lots of self-confidence.

As a wilderness guide, Keith Jardine is still meeting challenges and learning about himself, and so are the kids who go rafting with him. A girl who was frightened about riding on the river discovered that she could help steer the big rubber raft. When she finished the trip, she said, "I can really do this!"

Keith Jardine thinks that new experiences like river rafting are good for kids. He says, "It's one of my goals to help these kids succeed. They can use that feeling of success in whatever they do."

Keith Jardine's Tips
for Meeting New Challenges

 1 Learn all you can about what you're going to do. Ask questions.

 2 Make sure you have all the gear or materials you need.

 3 Tell yourself, "I can do this!"

 4 Even if you're afraid, give it a try.

Think About Reading

Write your answers.

1. What does the girl want to learn from Salguero?

2. What kind of person is the girl?
   How do you know?

3. If you visited the estancia, what would you
   most like to do? Why?

4. In what ways is life in *On the Pampas* different
   from life on a ranch in the United States?

5. How do you think the girl in *On the Pampas* would
   feel about going on one of Keith Jardine's raft trips?
   Explain your answer.

Write an Interview

You are a reporter for your class newspaper. Your job is to interview the girl in *On the Pampas* about her summer on the estancia. First, write two or three questions you want to ask the girl about her adventures. Then write the answers she might give. Be sure to include colorful details in the answers to questions.

Literature Circle

Ranch life and river rafting are both filled with challenges. What advice do you think the girl in *On the Pampas* might give to young people who are going river rafting? How would Keith Jardine feel about her advice?

Author
María Cristina Brusca

María Cristina Brusca really did visit her grandparents' estancia while she was on vacation. Like the girl in *On the Pampas*, she also dreamed of becoming a gaucho! Her dream came true when she wrote and illustrated the book based on her adventures. Now she lives in Kingston, New York, but she still has time to ride her horse in the nearby countryside.

More Books by
María Cristina Brusca

- *My Mama's Little Ranch on the Pampas*
- *The Cook and the King*

How to
Write a Friendly Letter

The **greeting** names the person you are writing to.

People like to keep in touch with friends and relatives who live far away. One way to do this is by writing a friendly letter.

What is a friendly letter? A friendly letter is a message written to someone you know and like. In it, you can describe events in your life.

The **closing** signals the letter's end.

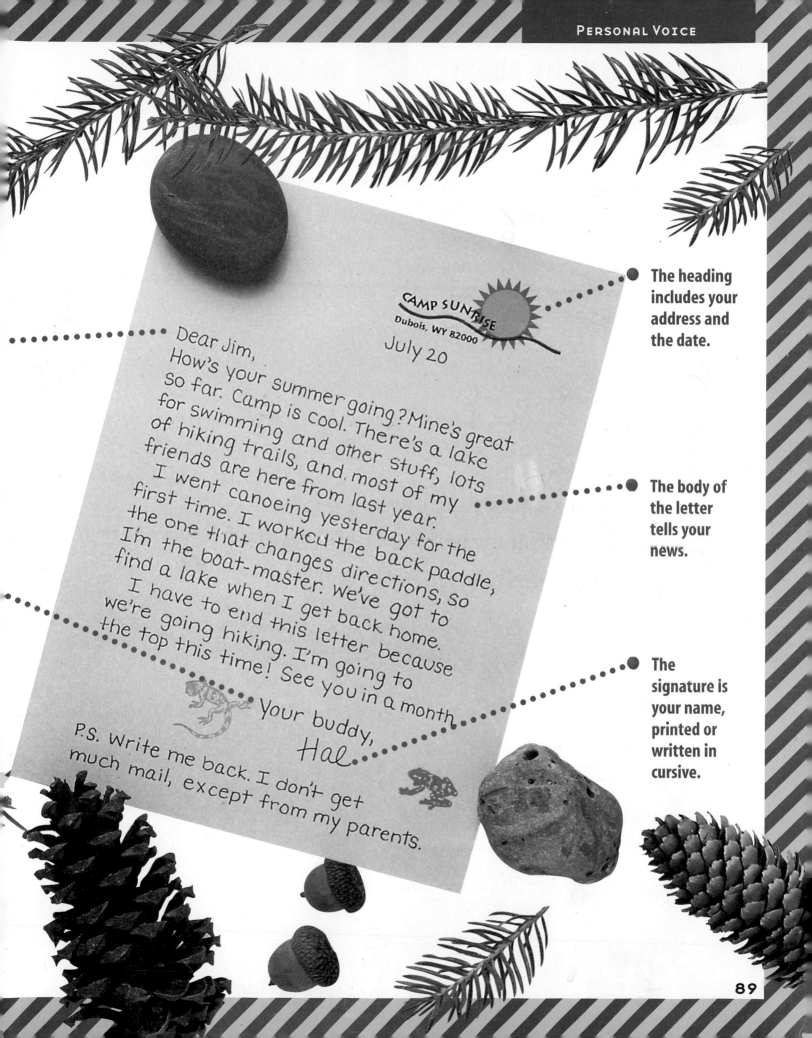

CAMP SUNRISE
Dubois, WY 82000

July 20

The heading includes your address and the date.

Dear Jim,

How's your summer going? Mine's great so far. Camp is cool. There's a lake for swimming and other stuff, lots of hiking trails, and most of my friends are here from last year. I went canoeing yesterday for the first time. I worked the back paddle, the one that changes directions, so I'm the boat-master. We've got to find a lake when I get back home. I have to end this letter because we're going hiking. I'm going to the top this time! See you in a month.

Your buddy,

Hal

P.S. Write me back. I don't get much mail, except from my parents.

The body of the letter tells your news.

The signature is your name, printed or written in cursive.

89

1 What to Write About

Think of some things you have learned to do recently, or a job you have finished or done well. Maybe you learned to use a computer, or built a birdhouse, or wrote a funny poem. List some of your achievements. Choose one achievement to write about in a friendly letter.

TOOLS

- pencil and paper
- envelope

2 Make a Rough Draft

Decide who will receive your letter. Will it be a best friend who moved away? a classmate at school? a favorite relative? Then, make a rough draft of what you want to say and include the following:

- Describe your achievement. Was it hard to learn? How long did it take you to do?

- Tell why it is important to you.

Now go back and reread what you have written. Are your thoughts clear? Is there anything else you want to say? Make your corrections.

Tip Remember, a rough draft doesn't have to be perfect. You can go back and make changes after you have finished it.

3 Write the Letter

Now write the final version of your letter. Use your best handwriting. You want your friend or relative to be able to read it. Remember, this is a letter to someone you know well. Make it warm and friendly.

Does your letter have:

- the date and your address?
- a greeting?
- a closing?
- your signature?

4 Send Your Letter

If you wish, you can show your letter to your teacher and classmates. Share your achievement with them, too. Then, address an envelope for the letter and put a stamp on it. Mail your letter to your friend or relative. If you're lucky, you'll receive a reply.

If You Are Using a Computer ...

As you revise your letter, use the electronic thesaurus to help you find just the right words. Choose a letterhead you like to create your own personal stationery. Then, use E-mail to send your letter on-line.

How to get to the waterfall

Hal Wong

CAMP SUNRISE
Dubois, WY 82000

Jim Smith
1 Main Street
Anytow

THINK

Most days are filled with achievements, big or small. What is one thing you have done well today?

Keith Jardine
Wilderness Guide ▶

WEST AFRICAN
FOLKTALE

FROM **THE ADVENTURES OF SPIDER**
WEST AFRICAN FOLKTALES

HOW THE WORLD GOT WISDOM

RETOLD BY JOYCE COOPER ARKHURST
ILLUSTRATED BY JERRY PINKNEY

NOW, WISDOM is another word for good sense. Nowadays there is wisdom everywhere in the world, but there wouldn't be any at all if it hadn't been for Spider's accident. Would you like to hear a story about it?

When the world was very new, Nyame, the Sky God, gave all the wisdom in the world to Spider, and told him to do whatever he wished with it. Of course, Spider wanted to keep it all for himself, and so he put it in a huge clay pot and covered it up tightly.

"How lucky I am to have all this good sense," thought Spider. "One day I will become a king, for I will be the only wise man in the world.

I must hide it carefully, where no one else can see it."

Spider ran through the forest as fast as his eight legs would carry him, looking for a place to hide his pot of wisdom.

"Where are you going?" asked the Tortoise.

"Where are you going?" asked the Hare. "And why are you in such a hurry?"

But Spider didn't answer. He just kept running, looking for a place to hide his wisdom before somebody saw it and took some of it away from him.

"I know what I'll do," said Spider to himself.

"I'll hide my wisdom in the top of the tallest tree in all the world."

At last he found just the tree. It was a great silk-cotton tree. At the bottom its roots came up above the ground and they were wide enough to hide an elephant. Its smooth trunk was wide enough for Spider's whole house. At the top the branches spread out like an umbrella, and they were covered with soft silvery leaves, and a fine gauze that looked like cotton. "It's the perfect hiding place," cried Spider. "No one will be able to climb it, because there are no branches near the ground."

So Spider went back to the place where he had left the pot of wisdom, and carried it to the foot of the great tree. Now, the silk-cotton tree is very hard to climb, for its outside is as smooth as a finger. But Spider was sure *he* could climb it. For one thing he had more legs than almost anybody else. People have two and animals have four, but Spider had eight.

Spider tied the pot around his neck with a piece of strong rope, so that it hung right in front of him. Then he made ready to climb. He put his two top legs around the trunk of the tree as far as they would reach. He put the next two legs around the top of the pot, two more around the bottom of the pot, and the last two under the pot. Spider pulled with his two top legs, and pushed with his two bottom legs, and held the pot with his four middle legs. My but the pot was heavy! After all it contained all the wisdom in the world. Little by little, he began to go upward. Spider was feeling very pleased, when suddenly he slipped. In fact, he fell all the way back to the ground.

"Dear me," thought Spider. "I have eight legs. Surely I can climb this tree."

So he started again. He hugged the tree as tightly as he could, and pushed and pulled with all his might. The pot was so heavy, and his two bottom legs just couldn't catch on under its weight. But this time, his luck was no better than before. He fell right back down to the ground. Spider was getting warm. And I'm afraid he was getting angry. He decided to try once again. So he pushed and pulled harder than ever. But the same thing happened. No sooner did he get off the ground than his middle leg slipped. Then his right upper leg slipped and his left top leg slipped and his right bottom leg slipped, and BOOM!

Down came Spider, pot and wisdom and all right on the ground again.

Now all this time, Kuma, Spider's eldest son, had been watching. "Father," said Kuma, "I have an idea. Hang the pot behind you instead of in front of you. Then you will be able to climb the tree."

When Spider heard this, he knew that Kuma had some wisdom too, and that he did not have all the wisdom in the world to himself. This made him so angry that he threw the pot to the ground. It broke into many pieces and the good sense poured out in all directions.

It made such a noise that people came from everywhere to see what it was. Old women came from the market. Men came from the farms, little boys came from their games, and little girls ran out of the round houses. And when they saw the wisdom pouring out of the pot, they all reached down and took some of it. Even the animals got some. They spread it all over the world. In India and Spain and Panama, where it is always hot or where it is always cold, everybody has some wisdom. Because there was plenty to go around. Plenty for you and plenty for me.

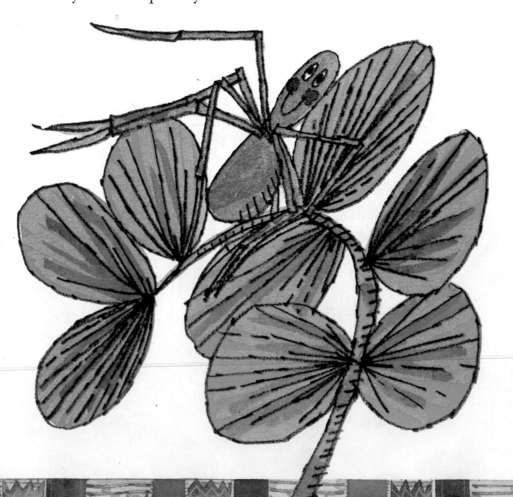

SPIDER GETS AROUND

Anansi the Spider is very popular in West Africa. Everyone likes this folk tale character because he is so wise. Anansi shows up on special beaded masks and hats. He is carved onto wooden bowls and around doorways. He appears on jewelry, stools, and walking sticks.

The Akan people of Ghana even have a saying about this clever character. "No one goes to the house of the spider Anansi to teach it wisdom."

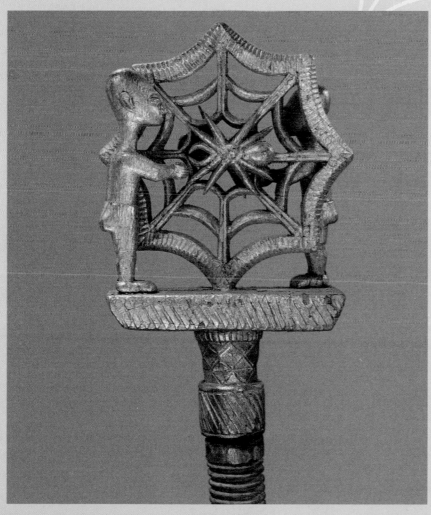

This gold-covered staff, or walking stick, is from Ghana. A wise person always carries this staff when there is something important to say.

from
ALL BEAUTIFUL THINGS

Parent to Child

By Naomi F. Faust

Your world's wide open.

Walk right in.

Drown yourself with knowledge;

drench yourself with skills.

The world's wide open, child;

walk right in.

THINK ABOUT READING

Write your answers.

1. Why did Spider want to climb the tree?

2. What kind of character is Spider? How do you know?

3. If you were Spider, what would you do with the pot of wisdom?

4. Why did the West African people tell this story?

5. How does the poet of "Parent to Child" feel about knowledge? How is this different from Spider's feelings?

WRITE A REVIEW

What did you like about *How the World Got Wisdom*? What would you tell another reader about it? Write a short review of this folk tale. Be sure to tell why you feel this way. Give the folk tale a rating.

LITERATURE CIRCLE

In *How the World Got Wisdom*, you meet one kind of spider. Think of songs, films, comics, stories, or other folk tales that have spiders. Tell what kind of character each spider is. Record your thoughts on a web. Then talk about how these spiders are different from the spider in the folk tale.

ILLUSTRATOR
JERRY PINKNEY

Jerry Pinkney started drawing when he was very young. He says this about his childhood: "I'd rather sit and draw than do almost anything else." Today Jerry Pinkney makes his living as an artist. He usually illustrates picture books about African Americans. He also likes the strong characters in folk tales. He says, "When I'm working on a book, I wish the phone would never ring."

MORE BOOKS ILLUSTRATED BY
JERRY PINKNEY

- *Black Cowboys/Wild Horses* by Julius Lester
- *Rabbit Makes a Monkey of Lion* by Verna Aardema

How to

Write an Anecdote

Tell a story about something that really happened to you.

Suppose a friend says to you, "You'll never guess what I did last weekend." When you hear these words, you expect to hear an anecdote about your friend's experience. An anecdote is a short story about an interesting or funny event. Personal anecdotes are interesting to hear, but they are even more fun to share. And everyone has at least one.

Did I ever tell you about...

What's Your Story?

Think of something that has happened to you that would make a good story. It might be about something that surprised you.

It might be about something you didn't like and then learned to enjoy. It might even be about going to a new place or meeting new people. Jot down possible ideas. Then choose the one you like the most.

TOOLS

- pencil and paper
- colored pencils, crayons, or markers

...and when I looked around...

2 Get the Facts

Think about your anecdote. Try to get all the facts straight. Then take notes about what happened. Make sure you know the order in which the events in your story took place.

Now go back and look at your notes. Decide which details in your story are most important or interesting. Did something surprising or funny happen to you? Did you find out something about yourself—what you can do or what you like to do? Now you have all the information you need to put your anecdote on paper.

How Am I Doing?

Before you write your anecdote, take a few minutes to answer these questions.

- Is my anecdote about something that happened to me?

- Do I remember the parts of the story that are important?

- Does my story have a good ending?

Write Your Story

Use your notes to write your story. Start out by briefly telling where the story takes place. Then tell what happened. As you write, imagine you are telling your anecdote to a friend. Try to make it lively. After you've finished, write the title and your name at the top.

Now illustrate your anecdote. Choose the part that you think is most important, and draw it. For example, if you won a prize, show yourself holding the prize.

Tip Personal anecdotes are always told in the first person. This means that you use the pronoun *I* when you tell your story.

What an ADVENTURE

4 Tell Your Story

Everybody loves to hear a good anecdote. Read yours to the class. Use lots of expression in your voice. Try to make your story sound exciting, funny, or scary. Display your illustration, too. Answer any questions your classmates may have about your anecdote.

that was!

If You Are Using a Computer ...

Tell your anecdote using the Record and Playback Tools on the computer. You can listen to your story as you write it. You may want to share your anecdotes with friends on-line.

CONGRATULATIONS

You have learned how new experiences can change you. They can make you feel good about yourself, too.

Keith Jardine
Wilderness Guide ▶

Big Plans

Big Plans

THEME
Making and using plans can help you solve problems.

UNIT 2

Welcome to

LITERACY PLACE

Construction Site

Making and using
plans can help you
solve problems.

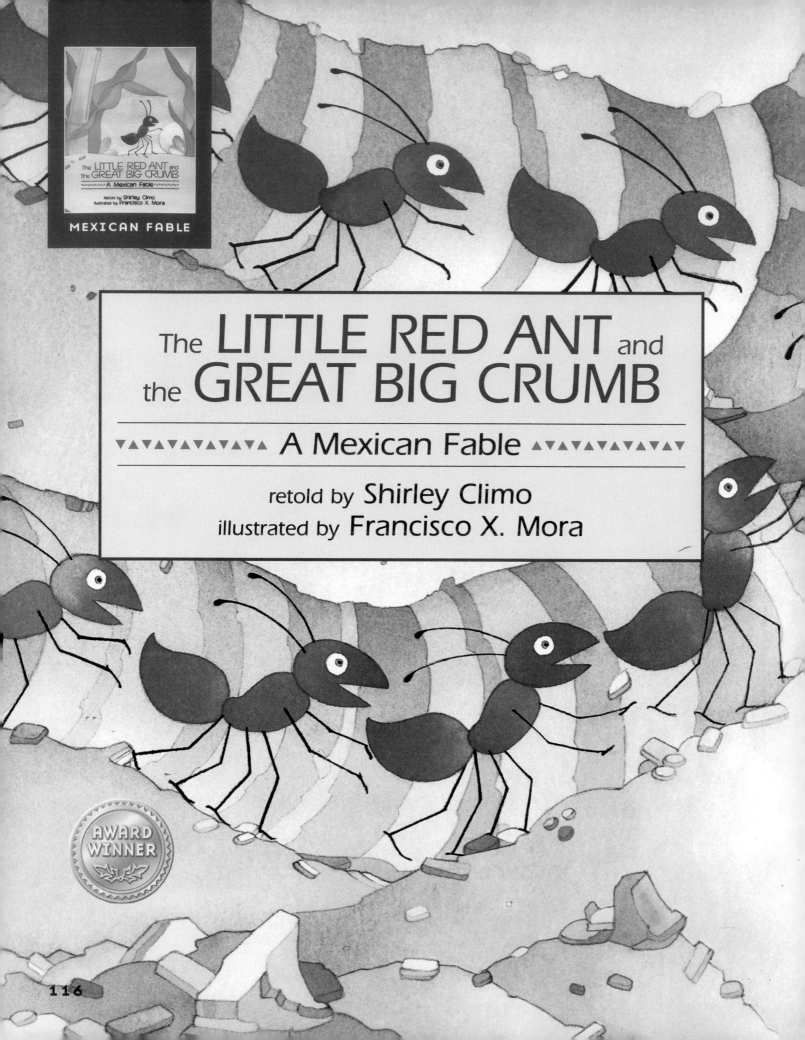

The LITTLE RED ANT and the GREAT BIG CRUMB

A Mexican Fable

retold by **Shirley Climo**

illustrated by **Francisco X. Mora**

Once, in a cornfield in Mexico, there lived a little red ant. She shared an anthill with her nine hundred ninety-nine cousins. They looked exactly alike except for the little red ant. She was a bit smaller than the others.

Early one fall morning all the ants crawled from
their anthill. They paraded single file across the
field, looking for food to store for the winter.
Because her legs were shorter, the little red ant was
last in line.

"¡Amigos!" she called. "Wait for me."

"Quick!" scolded the others. "¡Pronto!"

The larger ants began to return to the nest, carrying
scraps of corn on top of their heads. They left nothing
behind for the little red ant. Then she spied something
yellow under a leaf. It was the color of corn, but it
smelled much sweeter.

The ant guessed at once what it was.

"¡Torta!" exclaimed the little red ant.

Perhaps a bird had dropped the cake from the sky. Perhaps a mouse had dug it from the ground. But now this wonderful crumb of cake belonged to her.

"Lucky me!" said the little red ant.

She tried to push the crumb. "Oooof!" she puffed.

She tried to pull it. "Ugh!" she panted.

She sighed and said, "I need someone strong to carry my crumb for me."

The little red ant covered the cake with the leaf again. Then she set off down the row of cornstalks to find someone strong to help her.

The ant had not gone far when she spied a log.

"A log is nice for resting," she said, climbing up on it.

"Get off!"

The ant jumped down. She discovered a pointy nose at one end of the log. At the other end she found a twitching tail.

The ant guessed at once what it was.

"¡El Lagarto!" exclaimed the little red ant.

"Buenos días," the ant said politely to the lizard. "Good morning. I am looking for someone strong."

El Lagarto puffed his cheeks. "I'm so strong I can blow down an anthill!"

"Not that!" the ant cried. "I want you to carry my big crumb of cake."

"Too cold," grumbled the lizard. "I'm stiff as a stick until El Sol warms me up."

"Then El Sol is stronger than you are," said the ant. "I shall ask the sun to help me."

"We can wait for him together," El Lagarto whispered. He flicked out his long tongue. "Come closer."

"No, gracias," the ant said quickly. "No, thank you." She did not want to be breakfast for a hungry lizard.

The little red ant ran down the row as fast as her six legs would take her.

She had not gone very far when she spied a cobweb stretched between two cornstalks. Shining through the web was the sun.

"Lucky me!" cried the ant. "There is El Sol—caught in a net!" She scrambled up the stalk.

"Stop shaking my ladder!"

The little red ant spied something black and yellow skipping across the web.

The ant guessed at once what it was.

"¡La Araña!" exclaimed the little red ant.

"Perdón," said the ant to the spider. "Excuse me. I am climbing to the sun to ask him to carry my crumb of cake. El Sol is very strong."

"Foolish ant!" scoffed the spider. "No one can climb so high. Anyhow, I know someone stronger than El Sol."

"Who?" asked the ant.

"El Gallo! He wakes the sun every morning."

"Then I shall ask him to help me," the ant declared.

"Stay a while," La Araña coaxed, "and keep me company."

The little red ant gazed up at the spider. The sun had moved higher in the sky and no longer seemed caught in the web. A fly was caught instead.

"No, gracias," said the ant quickly. She did not want La Araña to tie her up like the fly. "No, thank you."

The little red ant backed down the stalk and hurried on her way. She had not gone very far when she stumbled over the roots of two tall thin trees.

"¿Qué pasa?" a scratchy voice demanded. "What's happening?"

The ant rubbed her eyes. She saw that the roots were really claws. She saw that the trees were really legs. She looked up and saw a fierce face with beady eyes bending over her. A yellow beak snapped open and shut, and a red topknot bobbed up and down.

The ant guessed at once what it was.

"¡El Gallo!" exclaimed the little red ant.

"Por favor . . ." the ant begged the rooster. "Please . . . don't eat me!"

"Ants taste HORRIBLE!" squawked El Gallo.

"Then will you carry my crumb of cake for me?"

"I'm too busy." The rooster cocked his head.
"Did you say cake?"

"Sí," said the little red ant. "Yes."

"Cake tastes DELICIOUS!" crowed El Gallo.
"I shall eat your crumb myself!"

"But . . ." the ant began.

"Where is it?" The rooster ran about in circles.
"Awk!" he screeched suddenly. "Listen!"

"To what?" asked the ant.

"To that dreadful noise! It's the chicken-chaser!
Awk!" Flapping his wings, the rooster flew up and
over the cornstalks.

The ant was glad to see El Gallo go before he found her great big crumb. "Lucky me," said the little red ant, and hurried on her way.

She had not gone very far when she came upon something big and bristly. Its nose was pointed to the sky, and the dreadful noise was coming from its mouth.

The ant guessed at once what it was.

"¡El Coyote!" exclaimed the little red ant.

"¡Hola!" the ant shouted to the coyote. "Hello!"

El Coyote stopped in the middle of a howl and stared down his nose at the ant. "Don't bother me. I'm singing the sun a bedtime song." The coyote threw back his head, ready to howl again.

"You must be strong to sing so loudly," said the ant. "Will you carry my big crumb of cake for me?"

"Not now," said El Coyote. "Maybe tomorrow. Or next week."

"But that might be too late!"

Suddenly the coyote pricked up his ears, and the hair on his back stood on end. "¡Mira!" he yelped. "Look! It is the terrible Hombre!" El Coyote tucked his tail between his legs and dashed off through the cornstalks.

The little red ant was sad to see him go. Then she
shrugged and started on her way again. But . . .
Something was moving down the row toward her.
It wore boots on its feet and a straw hat on its head.
The ant guessed at once what it was.
"¡El Hombre!" exclaimed the little red ant.

From far away, the man looked too small to help
even an ant. But the nearer he came, the larger he
got. Soon he was taller than the cornstalks, and his
shadow stretched halfway down the row. He grew
so tall that the little red ant could not even see the
top of his hat.

"¡Señor!" called the ant. "Please carry my cake for me."

The man did not hear her. He kept walking.

Now the little red ant looked up and saw something terrifying. The heel of his huge boot hung over her head.

"¡Alto!" exclaimed the little red ant. "Stop!"

The man did not hear her. He kept walking. So . . .

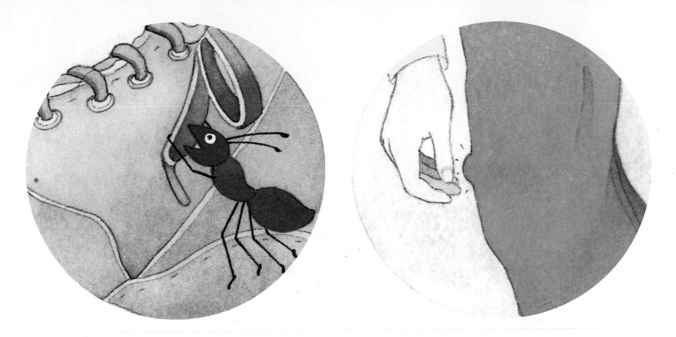

The little red ant took a skip and a hop and caught hold of his shoelace. Then she ran up his leg.

The man rubbed his knee. So . . .

The little red ant scurried under his shirt.

The man scratched his chest. So . . .

The little red ant skittered over his shoulders.

The man slapped his neck. So . . .

The little red ant crept into his ear.

She shouted in her very loudest voice, "HELP ME!"

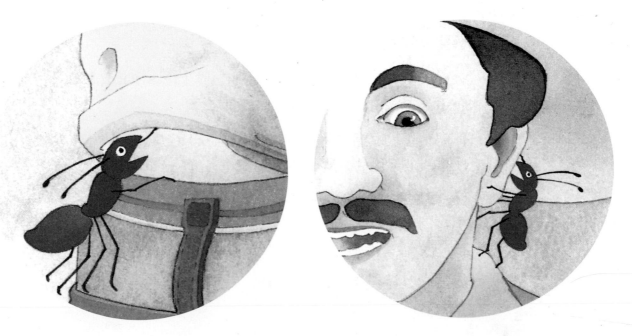

"Yi!" yelled the man. "Ticklebugs!" He shook his head and jumped up and down.

The straw hat flew from his head, and the little red ant tumbled down on top of it.

The man ran across the cornfield, still shouting, "TICKLEBUGS!"

The ant watched him go. "Adiós, señor," she called. "Goodbye." Then she thought of something quite surprising.

"I frighten El Hombre . . . who scares El Coyote . . . who chases El Gallo . . . who wakes El Sol . . . who warms El Lagarto . . . who can blow down an anthill. So . . .

"I AM THE STRONGEST OF ALL!"

The little red ant crawled off the hat. She followed her trail back through the cornstalks, just the way she had come. At last she reached her crumb of cake and pulled off the leaf.

"Aah," said the ant, sniffing. The cake was warm and sticky and smelled sweeter than ever.

She took a big, big breath. Then, ever so slowly, she lifted the crumb. She lifted it up and up until she could put it on top of her head. Then . . .

Step by step,
inch by inch,
all by herself,
by the light of the moon,
the ant carried her wonderful cake home
to the anthill.

She feasted on the crumb all winter long.
And, when springtime came . . .

she was exactly the same size as her cousins.

"Lucky me!" exclaimed La Hormiga, the ant.

Like all fables, this one has a moral.
You can do it if you think you can.

Characters

Spanish	Pronunciation	English
El Lagarto	el lahGAHRtoh	The Lizard
El Sol	el SOHL	The Sun
La Araña	lah ahRAHnyah	The Spider
El Gallo	el GAHyoh	The Rooster
El Coyote	el cohYOHtay	The Coyote
El Hombre	el OHMbray	The Man
La Hormiga	lah ohrMEEgah	The Ant

Other Spanish Words

Spanish	Pronunciation	English
Amigos	ahMEEgohss	Friends
¡Pronto!	PROHNtoh	Quick!
Torta	TOHRtah	Cake
Sí	SEE	Yes
Buenos días	BWAYnohss DEEahss	Good morning
Gracias	GRAHsyahss	Thank you
Perdón	payrDOHN	Excuse me
¿Qué pasa?	KAY PAHsah	What's happening?
Por favor	POHR fahVOHR	Please
¡Mira!	MEErah	Look!
Señor	SAYnyohr	Mister
¡Alto!	AHLtoh	Stop!
Adiós	ahDYOHSS	Goodbye

from *Something BIG Has Been Here*

Who Pulled the Plug in My Ant Farm?

poem by **Jack Prelutsky**

drawings by **James Stevenson**

Who pulled the plug in my ant farm?
Who let my ants get away?
Their tunnels are almost deserted,
I'm having a miserable day.
They've gathered in groups in the corners,
they're swarming all over the floor,
for each one I get in my clutches,
there seem to be two dozen more.

I'm doing my best to corral them,
I doubt that I'll ever be done,
there's nothing as hard to recapture
as hundreds of ants on the run.
My mother found ants in her slippers,
my sister found ants in her shoes,
they got in my father's pajamas,
he bellowed, "I'm blowing a fuse!"

Some have invaded the kitchen,
they've started attacking our food,
my mother is shrieking in horror,
and I'm in a horrible mood.
Who pulled the plug in my ant farm,
infesting our home with those pests?
I have the unhappy suspicion
that ants are our permanent guests.

Think About Reading

Answer the questions in the story map.

Setting

1. Where does the story take place?

Characters

2. Who is the main character in the story?

Problem

3. Why can't the little red ant carry the big crumb?

Events

4. What does the little red ant ask the other characters to do?

5. What do the other characters do for the little red ant?

6. What happens to make the little red ant feel she is the strongest?

Solution

7. How does the little red ant solve her problem?

Write a Letter

Write a letter to Francisco X. Mora. Tell what you liked about his illustrations in *The Little Red Ant and the Great Big Crumb.* Did any of the pictures make you laugh? Were you surprised by anything? Which picture was your favorite? Be sure to include your address, the date, a greeting, and a closing in your letter.

Literature Circle

Both the story and the poem are about ants. One is told through an ant's eyes, and one is told through a boy's eyes. Suppose the main characters in the story and poem changed. What would happen if El Hombre told the story about the little red ant? What would happen if the ants described their escape from the ant farm? Which version would you like better? Why?

Author
Shirley Climo

Author Shirley Climo loved stories even as a child. She says, "Long before I could read, I'd begun telling my own tales to myself and to anyone else willing to listen." Today Shirley Climo is still doing what she loves best—telling stories. She especially likes folk tales from around the world and has written three versions of the Cinderella story—from Egypt, Korea, and Ireland.

More Books by
Shirley Climo

- *Stolen Thunder: A Norse Myth*
- *The Irish Cinderlad*
- *The Egyptian Cinderella*
- *The Korean Cinderella*

FROM

THE BOOK OF THINK

(OR HOW TO SOLVE A PROBLEM TWICE YOUR SIZE)

BY **MARILYN BURNS**

ILLUSTRATED BY **MARTHA WESTON**

▶ ▶ ▶ ▶ ▶ ▶ ◀ ◀ ◀ ◀ ◀ ◀

There Are at Least Two Ways to Look at Something

It's easy to look at something. You see what you see. And that's the end of that.

But watch out.

That's you stopping you from exploring other possibilities. Getting in your own way.

A mirror reverses your image from left to right. Have you ever wondered why it doesn't reverse it top to bottom also? Have you ever wondered why you never wondered about that?

Optical illusions play tricks on your brain. They say, "Hey, look again. Something else is happening here." Then you look more carefully to see what it is.

There are some optical illusions that look absolutely possible. But they aren't. No matter how you look at them.

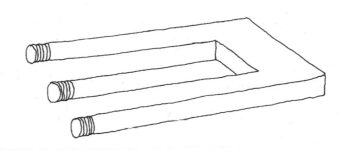

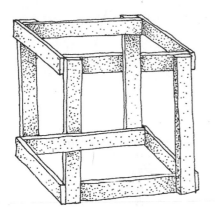

Some look like something they aren't. You can prove it to yourself.

Is the hat taller or wider?

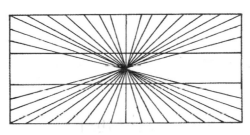

Are the curved lines curved?

Which line seems longer?

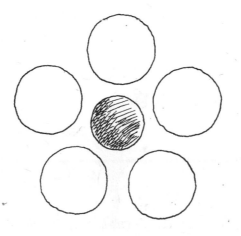

Which shaded circle seems bigger? Is it?

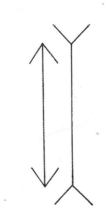

Which vertical line looks longer?

Some illusions can be looked at two different ways. Look at each for a bit. You will switch back and forth from seeing one thing to another.

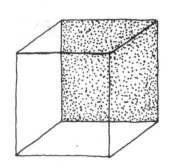

Is the shaded side inside or outside?

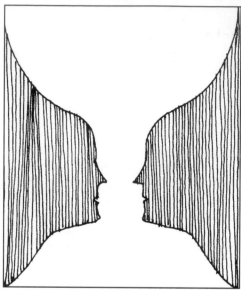

Do you see the profiles first or the goblet?

Which is easier for you to see—the rabbit or the duck?

Can you find both the old woman and the young woman?

The next step: Getting your brain to serve you that way when there's no optical puzzle. One way to practice is by purposely thinking about the same thing in more than one way.

Like this: Picture a glass half filled with water. Is the glass half-full? Or half-empty?

Try these.

Do the walls of a house hold up the roof? Or does the roof keep the walls from falling in? Or falling out?

Is the girl picking up the box? Or putting it down?

Is the boy jumping up? Or coming down?

Is the girl walking toward the tree? Or away from the house?

Brain Push-ups

In this section, you'll learn different ways to tackle problems. Also, you'll get plenty of problems and exercises for practice.

Don't just read. Do the push-ups. Try to figure out the problems for yourself. That feels best. Next best is when you figure them out with a bit of a hint. It's even okay to peek at the answer when you just have to know.

But most important is this: Look at how you think, and how you get stuck. When you've got a solution, try to figure how it can help you next time.

Don't Fall for What Pops In First

An exercise problem: Get a dollar bill and a quarter. Now, balance the quarter on the edge of the dollar bill. No props allowed.

Your first reaction is important. Imagine the quarter balancing on the edge of the bill. What do you see in your head? Could it really balance like that? With no hands?

If not, get that right out of your head! Take charge. Don't fall for your own first thought. Stand up to your brain.

Look, there's got to be another way. A quarter can't sit on that skinny edge. You've either got to do something with that quarter. Or with that edge.

(Hint: There is something you could do to that edge. A quarter really can sit on it. And comfortably too.)

If you've been reading along without a dollar bill and a quarter, you've cut down on your chances of solving this. Give your head a hand.

Here are two possible solutions:

Throwing out what pops in first is a useful way to attack some problems. It keeps you from stumbling into two mental holes. One is tunnel vision. The other is looking at something only one way.

Here is more exercise, while you've got that dollar bill and the quarter handy:

Get two glasses or tin cans that are the same height. Place them so your fist can fit in between. The dollar bill should reach across them.

The problem: The quarter needs to stand in the middle of the dollar bill which is stretched across the two glasses or cans.

Try it. No, the quarter can't rest on either glass. No, you can't move the glasses closer. Now, throw out what you just tried and look at it another way. The dollar bill isn't strong enough to stretch across and hold the quarter. What can you do about that?

Here are some push-ups. They seem different, but they all have one thing in common: what first pops into your head may be no use at all. You've got to do something else with what you're given. Put out those first thoughts. Look another way.

Toothpicking Triangles

You can make a triangle that has three sides the same length with three toothpicks. If you had six toothpicks, you could make two triangles. Actually, you could make two triangles with equal sides with only five toothpicks.

Here's the problem: Use six toothpicks and make four triangles that all have the same length sides.

Blowing Bits

There are five bits of paper in the palm of your hand. You need to blow them off. But one by one. How can you do this?

Face to Face

You need one sheet from a newspaper. How can two people stand on the same sheet, face to face, so they can't possibly touch each other? No, the people's hands aren't tied. And you can't tear the sheet of newspaper.

Puzzling Ping-Pong

There's a Ping-Pong ball in a hole. The hole is just a little bit bigger around than the ball. It's longer than your arm is. Or anyone else's arm. There are no long sticks around. What can you do to get the ball out of the hole?

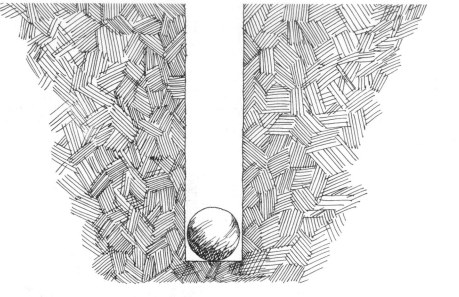

Practice ignoring what pops into your head first. Sometimes you may throw out an idea that was pretty good. But it wasn't getting you anywhere. Besides, there's always another way to look at something. That's the key. Looking at what's there in a different way.

Solutions

The answer to the dollar bill, the quarter and the two glasses problem: Fold the dollar bill like an accordion. Then it will hold the quarter.

The answer to "Blowing Bits": Just hold four while you blow one off. Then hold three. Blow again. And on and on.

The answer to "Face to Face": Any doorway will do. Place the sheet of newspaper so half is on one side of the door and half is on the other, with the door closed in between.

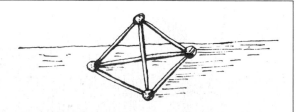

The answer to "Toothpicking Triangles": It can be done like this with clay. What made you think the toothpicks had to lie flat on the table?

The answer to "Puzzling Ping-Pong": Fill the hole with water. The ball will float up.

from
HIDDEN PICTURES
by Linda Bolton

Every picture tells a story, but some pictures tell more than one story—if you know exactly where and how to look.

FLYING FISH, SWIMMING BIRDS

This painting, "Sky and Water I," is by the twentieth-century Dutch artist Maurits Cornelis Escher. Look at the center of the diamond shape. What do you see?

from

Stories TO SOLVE

Folktales from Around the World

Told by
George Shannon

Illustrated by
Peter Sis

A DRINK FOR CROW

*O*nce there was a crow who had grown so thirsty he could barely caw. He flew down to a big pitcher where he had gotten a drink of water the day before, but there was only a little bit of water remaining at the bottom. He tried and tried to reach it with his beak, but the pitcher was too deep and his beak was too short. But just as he was about to give up, he knew what to do. He flew back and forth from the garden to the pitcher until he was able to drink easily from the pitcher while sitting on its edge.

What did the crow do?

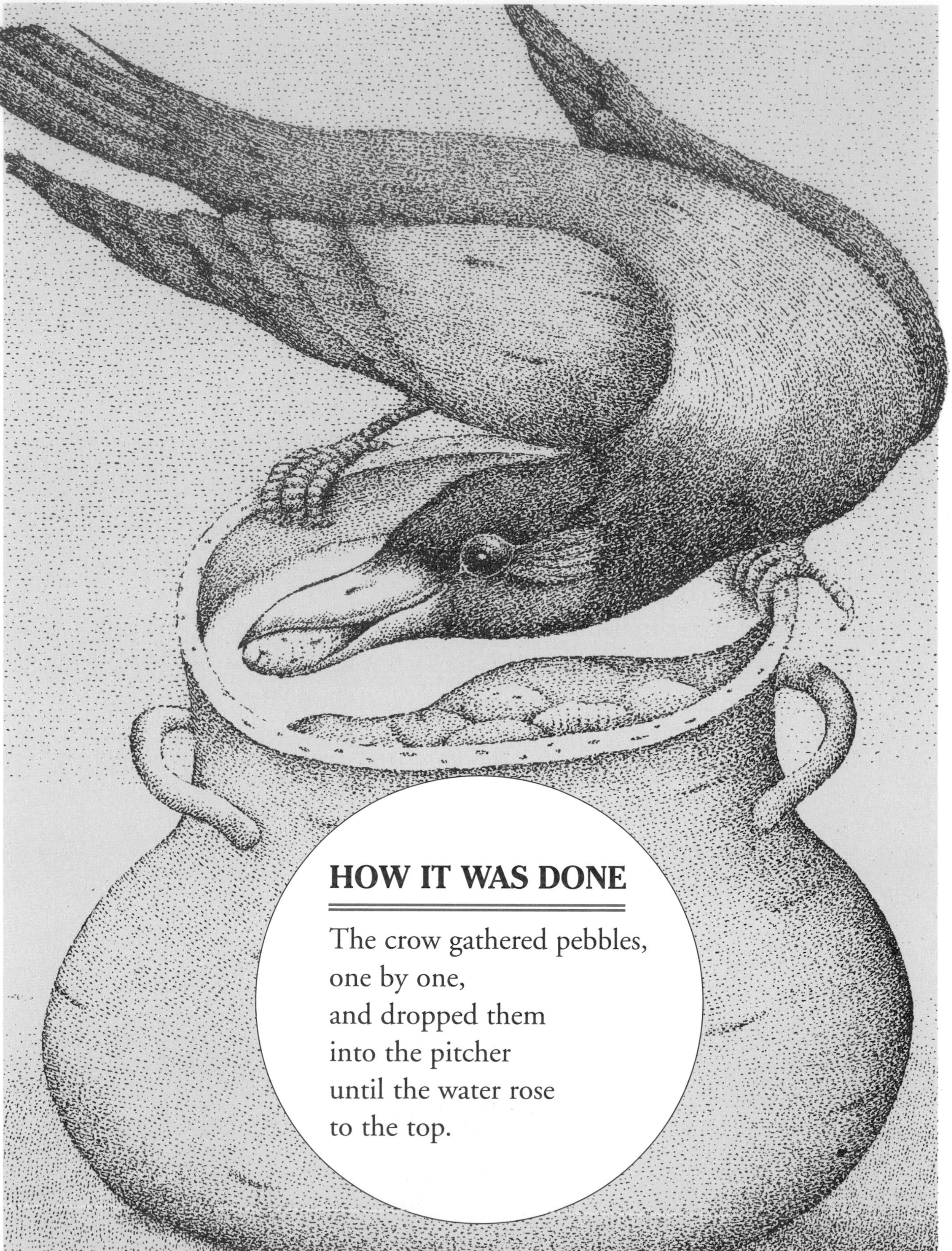

HOW IT WAS DONE

The crow gathered pebbles,
one by one,
and dropped them
into the pitcher
until the water rose
to the top.

CROSSING THE RIVER

Once there was a man who had to take a wolf, a goat, and a cabbage across a river. But his boat was so small it could only hold himself and one other thing. The man didn't know what to do. How could he take the wolf, the goat, and the cabbage over one at a time, so that the wolf wouldn't eat the goat and the goat wouldn't eat the cabbage?

SOLUTION 1

He could take the goat over

and go back alone.

Then take the wolf over

and then bring the goat back.

Then take the cabbage over and leave the goat behind.

And finally make one last trip

and take the goat over
to join the wolf and cabbage.

SOLUTION 2

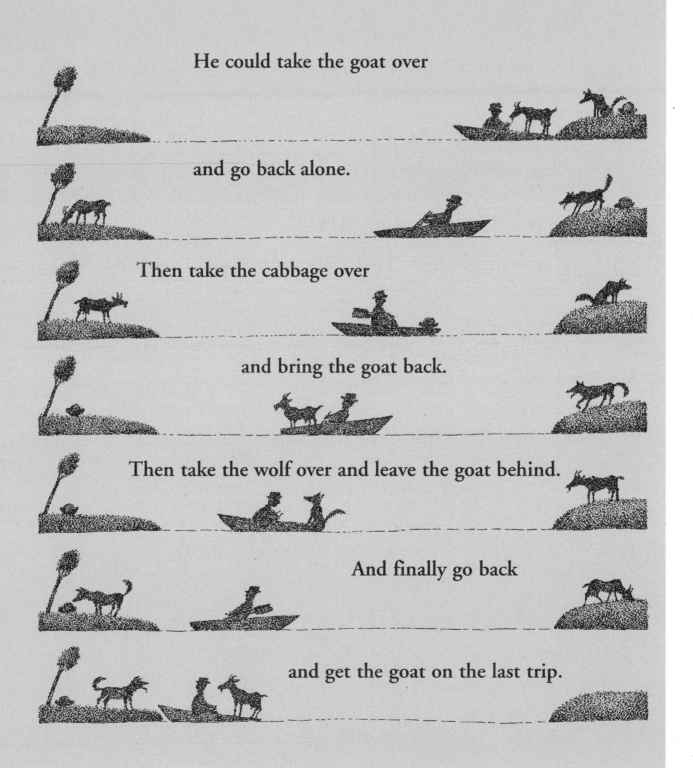

He could take the goat over

and go back alone.

Then take the cabbage over

and bring the goat back.

Then take the wolf over and leave the goat behind.

And finally go back

and get the goat on the last trip.

Think About Reading

Write your answers.

1. Why is it often helpful to ignore the first idea that pops into your head when you try to solve a puzzle?

2. What does the author mean by doing "push-ups" with your brain?

3. Why do you think a problem-solving guide like *The Book of Think* is important?

4. Why do you think Marilyn Burns put optical illusions and the brain push-ups in *The Book of Think*?

5. Which brain push-ups in *The Book of Think* can help you solve "A Drink for Crow"? Why?

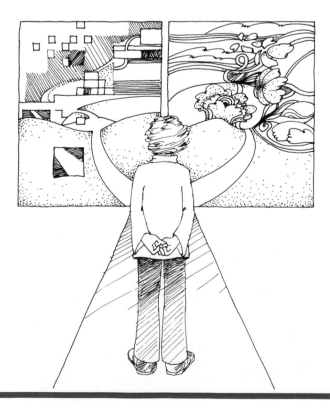

Write an Advice Column

Imagine that you are Marilyn Burns. You write a newspaper advice column for third graders. Here is a question that a reader sent you: *I always forget my books at school. Can you help me with this problem?* Write a letter to the student with an answer for the problem. Use what you learned in *The Book of Think* to help you.

Literature Circle

Think of the different puzzles in *The Book of Think* and in "Stories to Solve." Which ones were easier to solve? Talk about the ideas you had before you found answers to the problems. What did you do first? What did you do next? Were Marilyn Burns's suggestions helpful?

Author
Marilyn Burns

At the beginning of *The Book of Think,* Marilyn Burns says, "This book is for anyone who has at least one problem." Most of her books try to take the mystery out of problem solving. Ms. Burns writes about ways to solve all types of problems—even math problems. She began writing books to make problem solving fun. Her books, *The I Hate Mathematics Book* and *The Book of Think,* have won many awards.

More Books by
Marilyn Burns

- *The $1.00 Word Riddle Book*
- *The 512 Ants on Sullivan Street*
- *The Greedy Triangle*

How to
Design a Robot

People find different ways to solve problems. One way is to design and create special problem-solving robots.

What is a robot? Robots are special machines created to do jobs that people can't or don't want to do. Robots make people's lives easier and safer in factories, under water, and even in outer space.

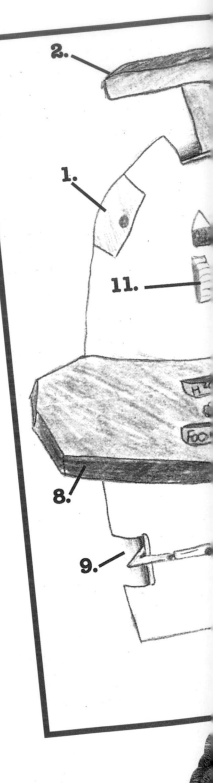

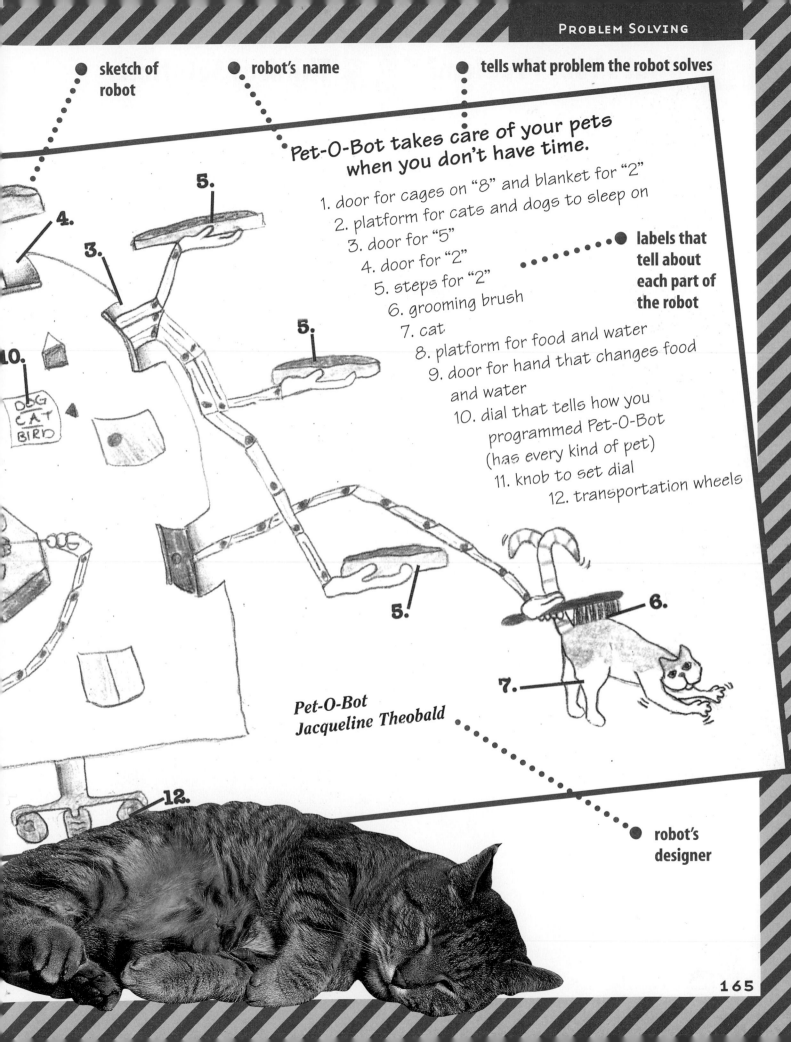

sketch of robot

robot's name

tells what problem the robot solves

Pet-O-Bot takes care of your pets when you don't have time.

1. door for cages on "8" and blanket for "2"
2. platform for cats and dogs to sleep on
3. door for "5"
4. door for "2"
5. steps for "2"
6. grooming brush
7. cat
8. platform for food and water
9. door for hand that changes food and water
10. dial that tells how you programmed Pet-O-Bot (has every kind of pet)
11. knob to set dial
12. transportation wheels

labels that tell about each part of the robot

DOG
CAT
BIRD

Pet-O-Bot
Jacqueline Theobald

robot's designer

1 What's Your Problem?

Think of several problems that you might face during your day. Maybe it's a messy bedroom, or litter on the street, or having to walk your dog on a rainy day. Make a list of problems you really want to solve. Choose the one that's most important.

TOOLS

- paper and pencil
- art supplies
- colored pencils or marking pens

Tips
- Clearly state what the problem is. For example, "picking up litter" is better than "fighting pollution."
- Brainstorm with a friend. Two heads are often better than one.
- Look at the problem from many different angles.

2 Think of Solutions

There is usually more than one way to solve a problem. For example, how can you keep litter off the street? How can this be done? One way is to pick it up right away. Another way is to stop people from dropping it. There may be other ways to solve the problem, too. Make notes about several possible solutions to your problem.

3 Create Your Robot

You have figured out some ways to solve a problem. Now design a robot that can carry out your solutions. For example, you might design a "Litter-bot." It sweeps up litter and reminds kids to throw their litter in a garbage can!

Draw your robot. Give it a name. Add labels that explain the parts of the robot. Write a sentence that tells the problem it solves.

4 Present Your Robot

With your classmates, put on a robot fair. Display your robot design. Be ready to answer questions about it. Now look at your classmates' designs. What kinds of problems do their robots solve? Do the robot designs from your class solve more problems at school or at home?

If You Are Using a Computer ...

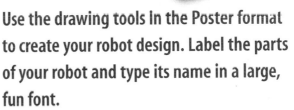

Use the drawing tools in the Poster format to create your robot design. Label the parts of your robot and type its name in a large, fun font.

THINK
Imagine that you are a robot. What kind of job would you like to do to help people? Why could you do it better?

Jack Catlin
Architect ▶

Dragon

in the Rocks

BY MARIE DAY

MILLIONS OF YEARS AGO WHEN DINOSAURS ROAMED THE EARTH, strange creatures swam in the sea. When they died, sand covered them where they lay on the ocean floor. Time passed. The ocean boiled and bubbled. Volcanoes erupted underwater, and the floor of the sea heaved up to form great cliffs.

Those ancient creatures vanished forever, and the cliffs became covered with trees and grass and wildflowers. Then people appeared. They settled in the pleasant places overlooking the sea. Two hundred years ago, in a little English seaside town called Lyme Regis, Mary Anning was born.

Mary grew up in a small house with her mother and father, her brother Joseph and her dog Tray. Early each morning Mary helped her mother make bread while Joseph helped his father saw wood in his workshop.

The little house smelled of fresh bread and new-cut wood and fragrant flowers, for Mary's mother always kept a bouquet on the table.

Mary's father made furniture to earn a living, but what he really liked best was collecting fossils. In those days a lot of people spent their time puzzling over these strange objects they found lying on the beach and buried in the cliff. There were odd-looking fish skeletons, giant seashells and even plants, all as hard as stone. How did they get there? Could these fossils be clues to the unknown world of long, long ago?

Mary and her father often went down the steep path to the beach. She loved the smell of the salt air and the sound of pounding waves. Sometimes, after a heavy rain, huge chunks of clay would fall from the cliff and crack apart as they landed on the shore. When Mary and her father examined the pieces they found mysterious bones and shells stuck inside them.

Mary learned from her father how to chip the rock-hard clay with a chisel and split it with a special little hammer. If she did it just right, a fossil would slide from the rock almost as easily as a baked cake slides from a greased pan. Mary's mother proudly placed the finest fossils on the mantelpiece where everyone could admire them.

"And where is my girl when I need help with sweeping floors or collecting eggs from under the hens?" she often said with a smile. "She's down at the shore collecting fossils!"

It was true. Every day, as soon as school was over, Mary wanted to rush down to the beach to search for treasure from the cliffs.

Mr. and Mrs. Anning sold many things on a stand in front of their house: lace and bonnets made by Mary's mother, tables and chairs made by Mary's father and Joseph, strange objects that Mary and her father had collected. "Come buy a fossil,"

Mary's father would cry. "The bone of an ancient crocodile! A flower, now turned to stone, that waved its petals at the bottom of the sea when the world was young!"

"Come buy a treasure," Mary would echo. "The tooth of a cruel shark that lived long ago! A shell that sparkles like gold!"

All their lives, Mary and Joseph had heard about a huge fossil trapped in the cliff. The great, grinning creature lay in a faraway cove where the sea crashed and foamed. Their father had been there.

Many an evening he would tell them about the strange creature in the rocks.

"Its teeth are like razors and its eyes as big as saucers," their father would begin. "It's waiting there now, grinning in the dark. It looks like a dragon. Its body is as long as a rowboat, and its head as long as a man."

"Take me there, Father," Mary always begged. "Please!"

Joseph wasn't nearly as eager. "Why get so excited over some old fish bones?" he would scoff.

It would be hard to count the number of nights Mary asked her father to tell about his journey to find the dragon. Again and again she heard about the treacherous climb up the slippery black cliff, how the sea soaked him through, how frightened he was, how he shivered with cold. How, when he was ready to give up, he saw the thing right above his head and stared into its great eye at last.

Mary longed for the day when she would see the giant dragon for herself.

One cold rainy morning Mary went down to the shore with Tray. Her father was very ill and could not leave his bed to search for fossils.

"Halloo, Mary," a voice rang out. It was her father's good friend, Captain Fossy. Everyone called him Captain Fossy because he spent every morning, noon and evening collecting fossils on the beach. His wide plumed hat had fossil shells sewn all over it. Captain Fossy had seen the great dragon too, and he said when she was big enough he'd go with Mary and her father to find it again.

As always, Captain Fossy rummaged in the deep pockets of his coat and brought out a present. "Something very special today, Mary," he said. He put a lovely, flat round stone in her hand. "A dragon's eye, I'm sure it is. Take it along and show your father."

"Oh, thank you, Captain Fossy. Father is so sick, and it will cheer him up," said Mary.

Mary came home to find the house strangely quiet. She held the dragon's eye stone tight in her hand. Tray wagged his tail anxiously and looked up at her. They both knew something had happened.

Then Mary heard the sound of someone coming downstairs. It was the doctor carrying his black bag, followed by her mother and Joseph, whose face was red from crying. The doctor put his hand on Mary's shoulder and patted it gently. "You must be brave, Mary," he said, "for your father has left us forever."

After a week had passed, Mary's mother spoke through her tears. "We are poor people. What will become of us?"

"I will go to the town of Axminster, where there is plenty of work," said Joseph. "It is not too far, and I will send money home every week." And Mary said, "Don't worry, Mother. I will leave school and spend all day finding fossils. Tray will help. We will sell them just as we always have. I know that is what Father would want."

Soon Mary was very busy. While her mother sold lace and bonnets on the stand outside the house, Mary went each day to find strange and wonderful fossils down at the shore. She took her discoveries to the busy place where the passenger coaches stopped to give the horses a rest on the way to Axminster.

While the horses rested, the passengers got out to stretch their legs, and Mary displayed her basket of fossils for sale. The ladies and gentlemen often left her with an empty basket and her pockets full of coins. Joseph sent money, as he had promised, and he came home often.

One fine summer morning when Joseph was visiting, he and Mary decided to go down to the beach. They stopped for a few moments on the cliff and watched the puffy clouds passing by in the blue sky. Suddenly they heard someone calling their names from the shore below.

It was Captain Fossy. "The weather is perfect for dragon-hunting," he shouted up to them. "The sea is calm as glass and the wind is steady."

Mary grabbed Joseph's hand, and they flew down the path to the shore. Tray jumped and barked alongside them. They were going to see the great fossil at last. Teeth like razors and eyes as big as saucers!

Captain Fossy led Mary and Joseph a long, long way along the rocky beach, and then they began to climb the steep, wet cliff. They clambered high over dark, slimy rocks and down past caves full of black shadows and crashing waves. Mary's heart beat fast as they edged across a narrow, slippery clay ledge that threatened to break off suddenly and fall into the sea. When they stopped to catch their breath, Mary looked back towards Lyme Regis. It was so far away the houses looked like little toys.

"When will we be there, Captain Fossy?" she asked. Captain Fossy shook his head. "I don't know," he said, gazing out to sea. "And now the wind is coming up. See, the tide is rising too! We'll have to turn back."

Just then Tray started to bark from somewhere right above them.

"There it is, there, look up!" Joseph shouted.

Half buried in the dark rock was the largest skeleton Mary had ever seen. It was more strange than the dragon in her dreams. It was as long as a rowboat. Its huge mouth was bigger than her whole body, and full of razor-sharp teeth. Its eye was much bigger than a saucer. It was bigger than her mother's biggest plate, the one that the Christmas goose was served on.

"We must go," Captain Fossy said. "Hurry now. The tide is rising fast." Mary was so entranced that she hardly heard him. When Joseph took her hand and pulled her away, she realized with a start that ocean waves were dashing over her feet.

The journey back was hard. More than once they had to scramble up the cliff as the waves grew stronger and crashed into foam just beneath them. When they arrived home, it was very late. Mary's mother scolded as she wrapped them in her warm shawl.

As Mary and Joseph dried themselves by the fire, they described every moment of their adventure. "I'm going to dig it out of the cliff. I know I can," said Mary when they'd finished their tale.

"Oh no, you can't," said Joseph. "It's huge, Mother, far too big a fossil for her to tackle."

"Nonsense, Joseph," their mother replied. "If your sister is determined to dig that creature out of the cliff, she will."

Soon, every fine day, Mary could be seen making her way down the beach. She always wore her father's old hat, to bring her luck. Little Tray was by her side. He liked to carry her basket of tools up and down the cliff.

While the tide was low, Mary chipped away at the rocks. When she'd carved out a few chunks, she would take them to a sheltered stretch of beach. There she hammered and pried at the rock-hard clay until the bones within were freed. Back to the skeleton she'd climb again, to start all over.

The weeks and months went by. The work was hard. As the hidden parts of the huge sea creature slowly emerged from the clay, Mary asked herself questions about it.

What was her dragon like when it was alive? What color was it? Green? Blue? Red? Striped, like a sunfish? What did it eat, down deep in the ocean? Even as it hunted, did even bigger creatures hunt for *it*? Was one of *them* trapped in the rocks, waiting now for her hammer to release it?

Mary had a plan to put the great creature together again. She had drawn a picture of the whole skeleton as best she could, and had given a number to each bone. Now as she chipped each bone from the rock, she numbered it. Then she carefully wrapped each one in plaster and cloth to protect it.

The baskets she carried back to her father's workshop at sunset each day were very heavy.

Sometimes strong stonecutters came to help Mary. They were used to hard work. They laughed and sang as they helped her chip the bones out of the rocks. They teased Mary with a tongue-twisting chant: *She sells seashells by the seashore.* It made her smile, even when she was very tired and her body ached from head to toe.

Finally, she pried the very last bone from the steep clay cliff.

Mary set to work cleaning the last bits of rock from each bone with small files and brushes. When that was done, she began to put the creature's bones together again like a huge jigsaw puzzle. She had numbered each bone so carefully that the creature took shape almost like magic on the floor of her father's workshop. Her mother brought her meals to her there, for she would not leave until the giant fossil was complete.

Word travelled all the way to the great city of London about a little girl who had dug a huge ancient creature out of a cliff. Many people didn't believe the story. How in the world could a child of twelve do that?

One day, five important scientists came all the way from London to see Mary. They crowded into her father's workshop and marvelled over the giant fossil. They were amazed to see how perfectly Mary had arranged the creature's bones, just as they had been in the clay. They could hardly believe their own eyes.

"Please tell me, what is this creature I have found?" Mary asked eagerly. The scientists explained that she had unearthed the rare skeleton of an ichthyosaur, a giant fish-lizard that had lived in the ocean millions of years ago. Like a whale, this mighty animal came to the surface for air. It had looked something like a dolphin, only much, much bigger, of course.

"Will you allow me to buy this remarkable fossil?" asked one of the men. "I'd like to take it to a famous museum in London where thousands of people can see it." Mary nearly cried from joy. How proud Father would have been of her!

That night, all the neighbors gathered on the beach to celebrate with Mary. Joseph brought a present for his sister, a chair that he had made himself, covered in red satin. Mary's mother gave her a lovely lace collar to wear. There was plenty of cake and cider and lots of singing. The blacksmith played his fiddle and the schoolmaster joined in with his accordion. Tray ran around and around in excitement.

Captain Fossy raised his cup high and shouted, "A toast to Mary, the greatest of all the fossil seekers!" Everyone clapped and cheered.

As the moon set and the stars became brighter, the people of Lyme Regis were still singing and dancing and talking about the great ichthyosaur. Mary was very happy. She just knew that there were other wonderful creatures to be discovered in the cliff. The next day she was going to set out to find them.

Mary Anning was a real person. With the help of her mother she continued to search for fossils, and she spent the rest of her life digging in the cliffs at Lyme Regis for mysterious creatures from the past. When you hear the tongue-twister "She sells seashells by the seashore," think of Mary Anning, for it is said that the "she" who sold the shells was her. And if you go to the Natural History Museum in London, look for a creature with teeth like razors and an eye much bigger than your mother's biggest plate—the one that the holiday meal is served on; and if the creature is longer than four men put together and has flippers shaped like paddles, then you too have found Mary's dragon in the rocks.

from Sing a Song of Popcorn

THE STEAM SHOVEL

by **Rowena Bennett**
illustrated by **Arnold Lobel**

The steam digger
Is much bigger
Than the biggest beast I know.
He snorts and roars
Like the dinosaurs
That lived long years ago.

He crouches low
On his tractor paws
And scoops the dirt up
With his jaws;
Then swings his long
Stiff neck around
And spits it out
Upon the ground . . .

Oh, the steam digger
Is much bigger
Than the biggest beast I know.
He snorts and roars
Like the dinosaurs
That lived long years ago.

Think About Reading

Answer the questions in the story map.

> ## Who
> 1. Who are the main characters?

> ## Where
> 2. Where and when does the story take place?

> ## Beginning
> 3. What do Mary and her father look for at the beach?
> 4. What does Captain Fossy show Mary?

> ## Middle
> 5. Why does Mary go to the cliff every day?
> 6. How does Mary put the dinosaur together?

> ## Ending
> 7. Why are the five scientists amazed?
> 8. What finally happens to the giant fossil?

5 Mary climbes a cliff every day because shes looking for fossils.

6 Mary numbered each bone and

7 then she started chipping

8 on it

7 The five sientist were amazed because its hard to find a full monsters bones.

8 The giant fossil was brought to the famous museum

Write A Poem

Think of a person or a thing in the story or poem that you want to describe. Then write a cinquaine about it. A cinquaine is a special five-line poem. To begin, list action words, describing words, and nouns that tell about your subject. Then follow the directions below.

———————
THE SUBJECT

———————   ———————
TWO DESCRIBING WORDS

—————— —————— ——————
THREE ACTION WORDS

——— ——— ——— ———
FOUR MORE DESCRIBING WORDS

———————
ANOTHER WORD
FOR THE SUBJECT

Literature Circle

Both *Dragon in the Rocks* and "The Steam Shovel" talk about dinosaurs. What other dinosaur stories have you read, seen in the movies, or watched on TV? Make a list. Talk about how they are alike. Which ones are most like Mary Anning's story? Why?

Author
MARIE DAY

Author and artist Marie Day likes nothing better than exploring and drawing new places. On a painting trip to England, she discovered the fossil-filled cliffs of Lyme Regis. Then she heard the story of Mary Anning's ichthyosaur. Inspired by the young paleontologist's story, Day returned home to Canada and wrote a book about her.

MORE BOOKS ABOUT
DINOSAURS

- *Digging Up Dinosaurs* by Aliki
- *Dinosaurs* by Lee Bennett Hopkins

Thousands of people want to work and live on the empty city block. It is a small space for so many people. A skyscraper must be built.

A **core sample** is taken to see what is underneath the soil. This tells the builders what kind of foundation to build.

The **owner** will pay for the construction of the skyscraper.

The **city inspector** gives the owner a **building permit,** or permission to build.

Surveyors measure where the foundation will be.

First, a site survey is done to study the ground for the *foundation*, the part of the skyscraper below the ground.

The **foundation engineer** designs the foundation.

The **weight** of the building is figured.

Plans for the foundation . . .

Architects design the skyscraper.

and for the rest of the skyscraper are made.

The **wind load** is how hard the wind blows against the skyscraper.

The **dead load** is the weight of the skyscraper alone.

The **exterior** is the outside of the building.

The **superstructure** is the part of the skyscraper that is aboveground.

The **live load** is the weight of the people, furniture and equipment.

The **interior** is the inside of the building.

The **framework** is the steel skeleton of the skyscraper.

substructure, or foundation

The **general contractor** schedules delivery of all equipment, workers and supplies to the site.

portable toilet

Pile drivers force the piles into the ground.

construction workers

Piles are large pillars of steel.

Bedrock is the solid layer of rock under the ground

After many months of planning, construction begins. The hole for the foundation is dug. It becomes deeper . . .

and deeper. Piles are driven into the ground until they hit bedrock.

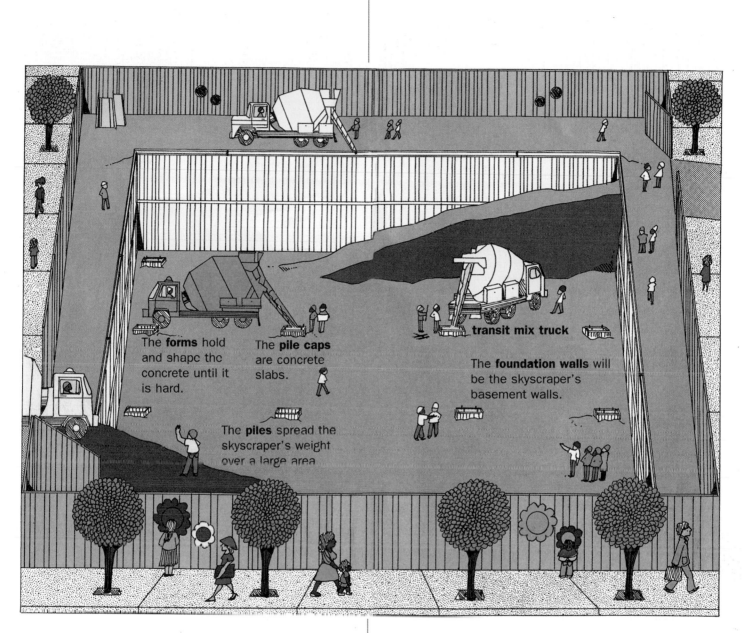

The **forms** hold and shape the concrete until it is hard.

The **pile caps** are concrete slabs.

The **piles** spread the skyscraper's weight over a large area.

transit mix truck

The **foundation walls** will be the skyscraper's basement walls.

Concrete is poured into wooden forms that have been placed on top of each pile to make pile caps. Metal rods stick out from each pile cap.

At the same time, forms for the outer foundation wall are built. Transit mix trucks come day and night to fill the forms.

When the concrete in the pile caps is hard, anchor bolts are connected to the metal rods. The cement floor of the basement is poured and smoothed over.

Cranes arrive at the scene to swing columns into position. Then, the columns are bolted to the pile caps. This is the beginning of the framework.

The **floorbeams (girders)** are in the shape of an I.

Ironworkers bolt the columns and beams together.

crane

When the columns are in place, they are connected by floorbeams.

Metal sheets make up the **decking** that supports the concrete floor slab.

Wire mesh makes the concrete stronger.

The framework is shaped like a box. Metal decking is welded to the top of the framework. Wire mesh is placed on top of the decking and concrete is poured. This becomes the ceiling of one level and the floor of the one above it.

199

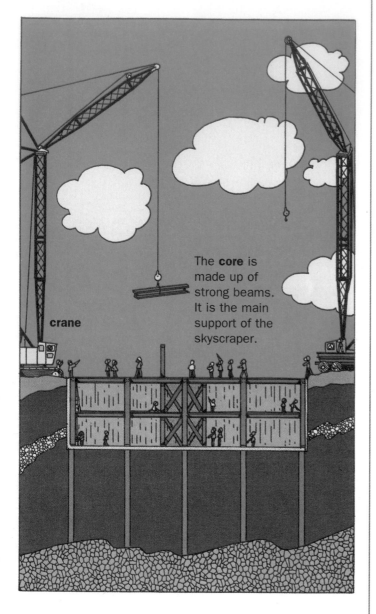

The **core** is made up of strong beams. It is the main support of the skyscraper.

crane

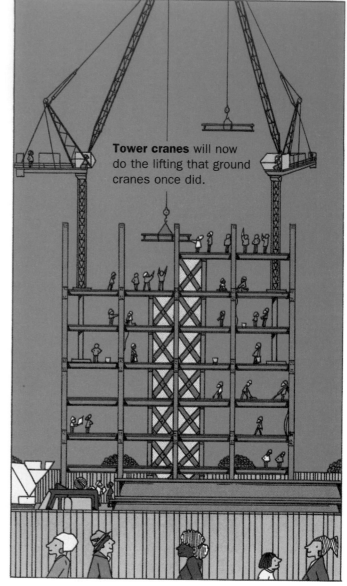

Tower cranes will now do the lifting that ground cranes once did.

The same thing is done again. Now the substructure is at ground level. In the center a core is begun. It is the strongest part of the skyscraper—the skyscraper's backbone.

Each day the general contractor has scheduled what materials will be needed. Trucks arrive. The ironworkers add another floor . . . and another . . . and another. Tower cranes are put into place. Each floor connects into the core. The tower cranes are raised each time two levels are completed.

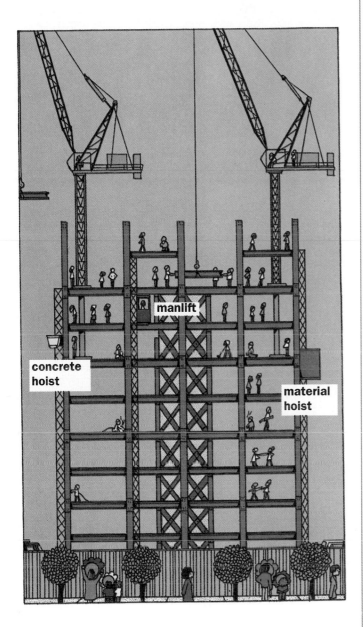

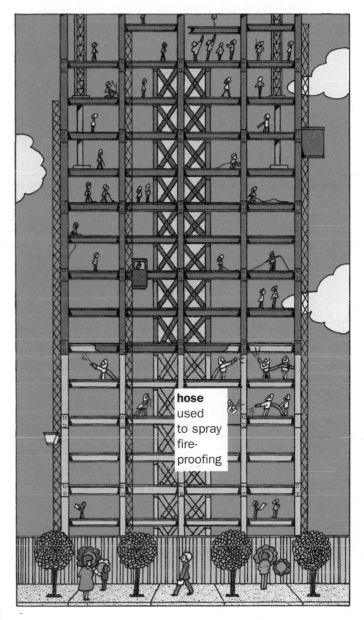

Up goes the skyscraper! People stop to watch. Workers go up and down on a manlift. Hoists are added to bring up concrete and materials.

While the ironworkers are building above, other workers are fireproofing the beams below.

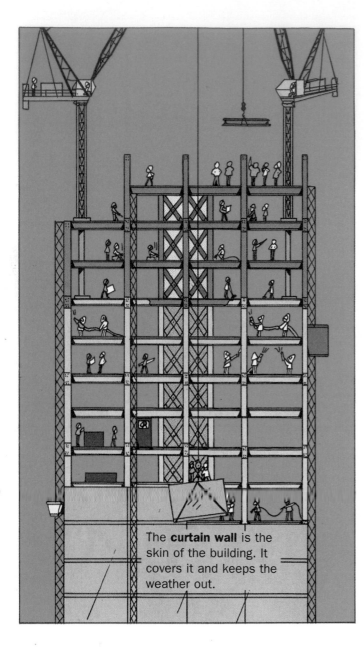

The **curtain wall** is the skin of the building. It covers it and keeps the weather out.

The tower cranes go up again. More beams are bolted into place. Below, where the fireproofing has been done, the curtain wall and windows are installed.

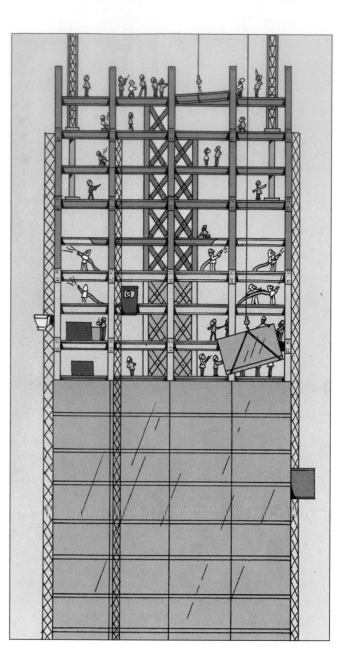

More floors are added.

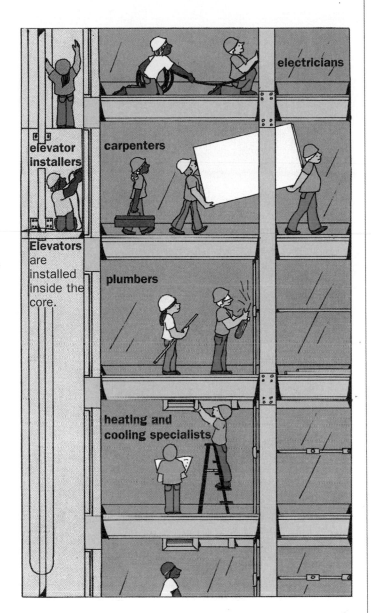

electricians

elevator installers

carpenters

Elevators are installed inside the core.

plumbers

heating and cooling specialists

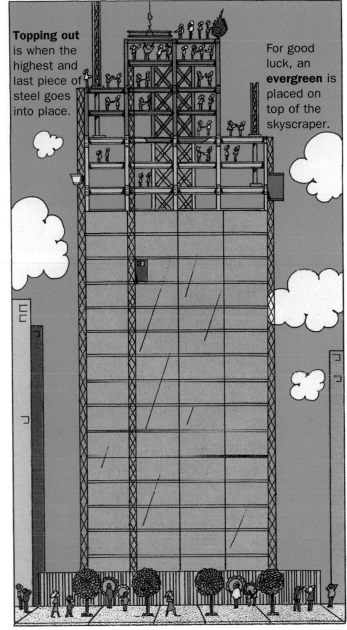

Topping out is when the highest and last piece of steel goes into place.

For good luck, an **evergreen** is placed on top of the skyscraper.

Finish workers—carpenters, plumbers, electricians, elevator installers, and heating and cooling specialists—are working below. Interior walls are added to the superstructure.

The ironworkers complete the last level. The last beam swings into place. Since it is last, it is very special. The workers celebrate the topping out. The finish workers keep on working . . . until the skyscraper is finally finished from the bottom to the top.

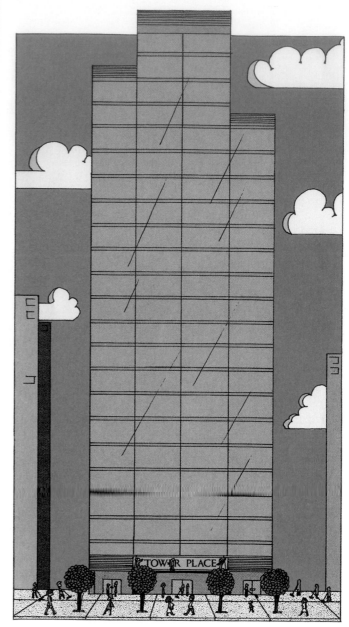

Next, the interior is designed. Fixtures and telephones are installed and sprinkler systems are added for fire safety.

The old wooden wall with its peepholes is torn down. The area around the skyscraper is tidied up. A plaque with the skyscraper's name is put into place.

For many months people have been watching the construction. Some have decided to rent space in the skyscraper for their businesses and homes.

Tenants are moving into the shiny new building.

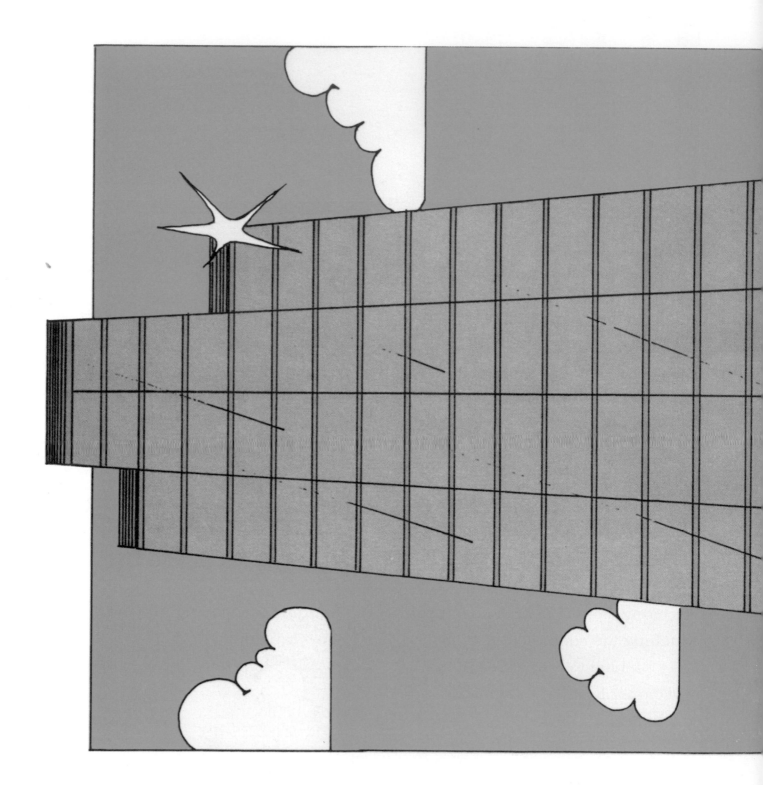

Look up at the skyscraper. It took two years to build and three hundred people to build it . . . and it is beautiful.

Jack Catlin

Architect

Designing buildings is like putting together a huge jigsaw puzzle.

Towering skyscrapers, huge sports arenas, and giant malls—how are they built? Ask architect Jack Catlin. He designs big buildings and makes sure they are put together correctly. But that's not all that he does. He solves big problems, too.

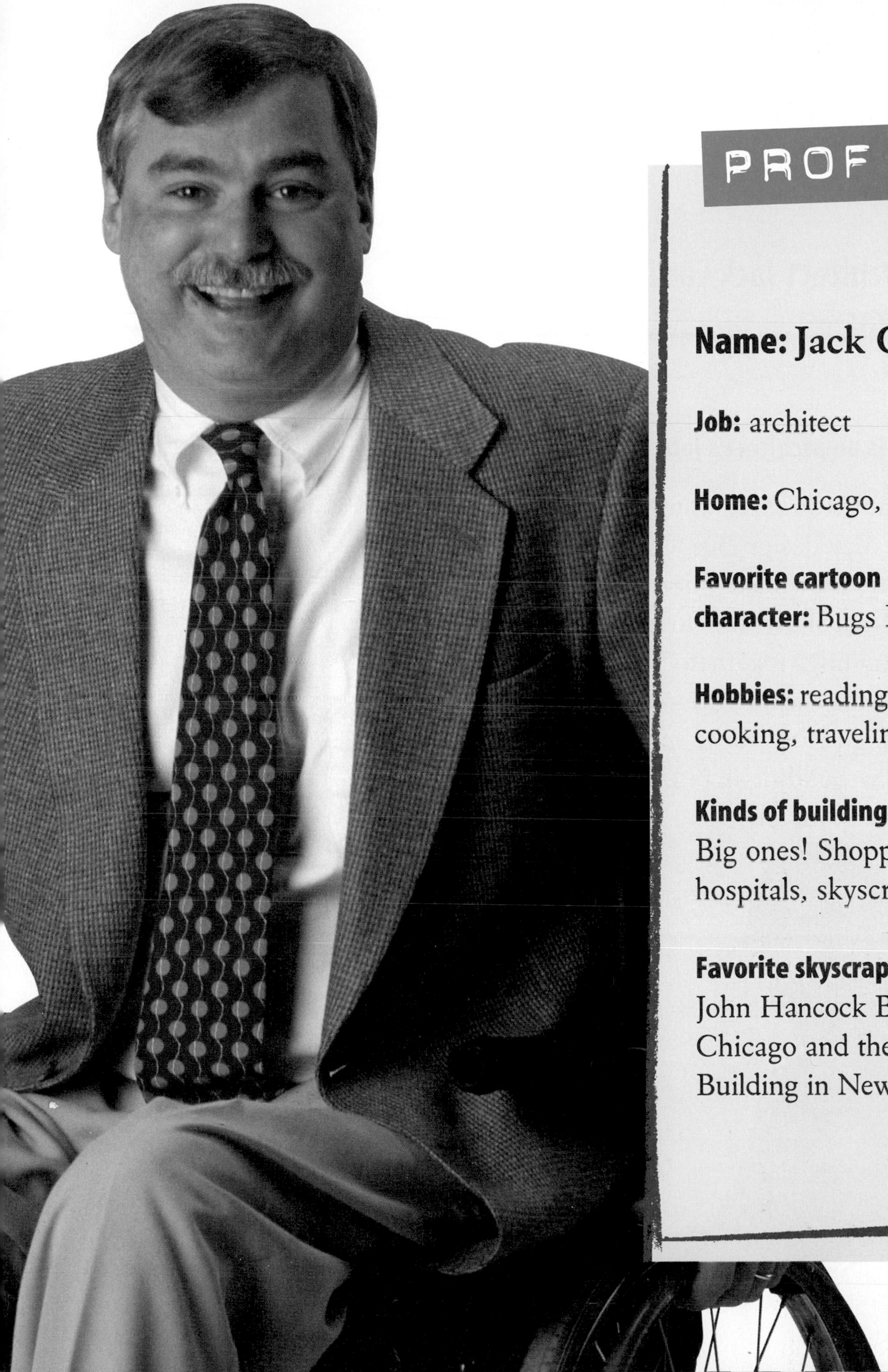

PROFILE

Name: Jack Catlin

Job: architect

Home: Chicago, Illinois

Favorite cartoon character: Bugs Bunny

Hobbies: reading, cooking, traveling

Kinds of buildings he designs: Big ones! Shopping malls, hospitals, skyscrapers

Favorite skyscrapers: the John Hancock Building in Chicago and the Chrysler Building in New York City

QUESTIONS
for Jack Catlin

Here's how architect Jack Catlin solves problems— big and small.

Q **What is an architect's job?**

A Architects do three things. First, they design buildings. Second, they make floor plans that show how to put the buildings together. Third, they work with a building contractor to make sure the building is put together correctly.

Q **Why did you decide to become an architect?**

A I liked buildings, even as a kid. But I didn't really notice them until about 20 years ago. After an accident, I lost the use of my legs. Suddenly, I found it difficult to go places in a wheelchair. Then I decided to become an architect. I wanted to design buildings that everyone could use—including people with disabilities.

Q **What was the first thing you built?**

A When I was about eight, I built a stone fort with my brother and a friend. We built a wagon to carry the stones about 300 feet. And we made a road of boards for the wagon to roll on. It was a big job. But in the end, we had a great fort.

Q What is a problem you have recently solved?

A I have been working on a huge mall near Chicago. In the mall's garden area is a gazebo. A gazebo is a small building with no walls where people can sit. The problem was that people had to climb steps to reach the gazebo. That meant that many people—ones in wheelchairs and ones who have trouble walking—couldn't sit in the gazebo.

Q How did you solve the problem?

A First I brainstormed with two other architects. We figured out three different ways to solve the problem.

We could put in a lift, a small elevator. We could build a ramp. Or we could lower the gazebo and take out the steps. We made drawings to decide which solution to use. Lowering the gazebo worked best. Now everyone can enjoy the gazebo.

Jack Catlin's Tips
for Solving a Problem

1 Understand the problem. Look at it from every side.

2 Find out as much as you can about the problem. Talk to people. Get their ideas.

3 Don't give up. If you need to, start over. Keep trying until you find a solution.

THINK ABOUT READING

Write your answers.

1. It takes many jobs to build a skyscraper. Name three of them.

2. Why are skyscrapers found in big cities but not in small towns?

3. If you were going to help build a skyscraper, which job would you choose? Explain your answer.

4. Why do you think Gail Gibbons used pictures, captions, and diagrams in *Up Goes the Skyscraper*?

5. What are three things that architect Jack Catlin does when he works on a skyscraper?

WRITE A FLYER

Now the skyscraper is built! Make a flyer inviting people to tour the finished building. Give the building's name and address. You may want to tell why the skyscraper is special. Include why it would be a good place to live or work. Remember—the flyer should make the skyscraper seem exciting.

LITERATURE CIRCLE

Think of the stone fort that Jack Catlin built when he was eight years old. How was building the stone fort like building a skyscraper? How was it different? Write your findings on a Venn diagram.

AUTHOR
GAIL GIBBONS

When Gail Gibbons was ten, she wanted a dog. She couldn't have one in the apartment where she lived. Instead of getting a real dog, she wrote a picture book about a girl who could have a pet. Today Gail Gibbons is still writing and solving problems. She says, "To me, putting a nonfiction book together is like watching the pieces of a puzzle finally fitting together."

MORE BOOKS BY GAIL GIBBONS

- *Catch the Wind! All About Kites*
- *Beacons of Light: Lighthouses*
- *Marshes & Swamps*

How to

Create Step-by-Step Directions

tells what the directions are for

lists materials

How do you learn to make a snowflake from paper? or use a computer? or make an after-school snack? One way is to follow step-by-step directions.

What are step-by-step directions? Step-by-step directions tell you exactly how to do something. They show the order in which you must do the steps. You can find step-by-step directions in books, magazines, and sometimes newspapers.

HOME TWEET HOME

FEATHER WATCH!

Make a Feeder Bag to bring on the birds!

YOU NEED:
1/2 cup peanut butter
1/2 cup birdseed
1 cup cornmeal
Bowl
Plastic net bag from fruits or vegetables

1. Put the peanut butter, birdseed, and cornmeal in the bowl. Use your fingers to mix them well.

2. Put the mix in the bag. Knot the bag closed.

3. Tie or hang your Feeder Bag where birds can perch — on a tree branch or a windowsill.

4. Wait a few days, then watch for birds. How can you tell what kinds of birds you see?

pictures the finished product

clearly numbers and explains each step

215

1　Choose Your Subject

Choose one thing you know how to do. It might be something you do at home or at school. Make sure the directions for doing it have several steps. They could be directions for making a sandwich, folding a paper airplane, setting the table for dinner, or tying a knot. You'll be surprised by how many steps there are in even the simplest activities.

TOOLS

- pencil and paper
- colored pencils or marking pens

2　How You Do It

You may have done something many times. But you might not remember all of the steps and details. When writing directions, you need to know exactly what to do and when to do it.

Tip Do the thing you're writing directions for. Make careful notes about each step. Write down everything you do. If you need to, make diagrams. And be sure to list all the materials and tools you need.

3 Write Your Directions

Now that you have all the information, writing directions will be easy.

• Give your directions a title.

• List any materials you need.

• Write out and number the steps for your directions. Try to make them clear and easy to follow.

• Make drawings for the steps that need to be illustrated.

Tip Do your directions work? Ask a friend to follow your directions. Notice any steps that don't work, and correct them.

4 Make a How-to Book

With your classmates, make a "how-to" book. Put directions for things that you make in one section, directions for things that you do in another, and so on. Then look at your classmates' directions. Are they clear and easy to read? Do all the steps make sense?

If You Are Using a Computer . . .

Design a cover for your "how-to" book, using borders and clip art. Then type your directions, using the Report format on the computer. Print out the cover and your directions to make your "how-to" book.

THINK
Directions make doing things easier. What kinds of directions do you follow every day in your classroom?

Jack Catlin
Architect ▶

A Picture Book of Thomas Alva Edison

by David A. Adler

illustrated by John & Alexandra Wallner

Thomas Alva Edison was born on February 11, 1847, in Milan, Ohio. His parents were Samuel and Nancy Edison. Samuel Edison owned a mill which made wood shingles. Nancy Edison had been a teacher. Thomas was the youngest of their seven children.

Thomas was curious and asked his parents many questions. If they didn't know an answer, he asked, "Why don't you know?"

Thomas loved to experiment. He made a nest and filled it with goose and chicken eggs. He sat on the eggs to see if they would hatch. Of course they didn't. The eggs broke and ruined the seat of his pants.

Thomas was not a healthy child. He had many colds and when he was eight he had scarlet fever. He was deaf later, perhaps because of these early illnesses.

In 1854 the Edison family moved to Port Huron, Michigan. There seven-year-old Thomas went to school for the first time.

In class Thomas was restless. He didn't pay attention to the lessons. And he asked lots of questions. His teacher, Reverend Engle, had no patience for Thomas. He felt the boy was not smart enough to learn his lessons.

Thomas's mother told Reverend Engle that he didn't know how to teach a curious child. After three months, she took Thomas out of school and taught him herself.

Later Thomas went to two other schools. He once got into trouble for bringing a noisy chicken to class. But he did learn.

At home Thomas set up a laboratory in the cellar.
Strange smells, smoke, and sometimes the sounds of
small explosions came from there. Thomas was
finding answers to some of his many questions.

Beginning in 1859, when Thomas was twelve,
he worked as the candy butcher on the Grand Trunk
Railroad. He sold candy, sandwiches, fruit, and
newspapers to passengers.

Thomas set up a laboratory in the baggage car.
He did experiments during the long stopover in
Detroit. But Thomas didn't take proper care of the
chemicals, and one day there was a fire. The baggage
master quickly put it out. Then he threw the
chemicals off the train.

In 1862 Thomas bought a secondhand printing press and some type. He set the press up in the baggage car and printed his own newspaper, the *Weekly Herald*. In it he printed news of people who traveled and worked on the train.

Thomas also wrote his opinions. He believed in work and wrote, "The more to do, the more done."

At each train stop, Thomas got off and sold newspapers to people near the station. With the money he earned, Thomas bought more chemicals for his experiments.

One morning, in 1862, at the Mount Clemens station, Thomas saw a boxcar rolling toward a small boy. Thomas dropped his things, ran, and saved the child. The boy's father rewarded Thomas by teaching him telegraphy. After that, beginning in 1863, Thomas worked for almost six years as a telegraph operator.

In 1869 Thomas moved to New York City. While he was there, he visited a company that sent out minute-by-minute information about changes in the price of gold. When the equipment in that office broke, Thomas quickly found the trouble and fixed it. He was given a high-paying job taking care of the company's equipment.

A few months later, Thomas and a friend formed their own company. They made electrical devices for telegraphy. Thomas Edison worked from early morning until late at night. He invented a telegraph that printed the price of gold and silver.

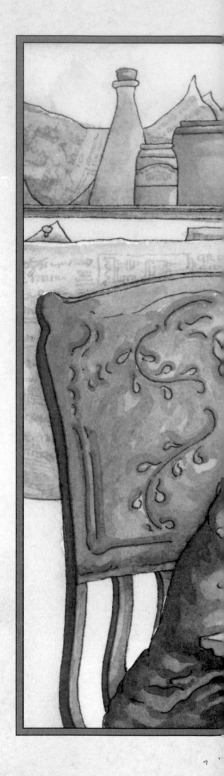

Then Thomas went to work for himself. He invented an improved machine to send out minute-by-minute information on the price of stocks. He sold it to Western Union. With the money he set up a laboratory in Newark, New Jersey.

Thomas Edison worked on improving the telegraph. Among his inventions was an automatic telegraph system. It didn't need a telegrapher to take down the messages. He also invented the quadruplex, which could send four messages at the same time over one wire.

Edison's company sold printers to the Gold and Stock Company. In 1871 Thomas helped a friend's sister get a job there. She was a pretty sixteen-year-old named Mary Stilwell. Thomas kept stopping by Gold and Stock to check the printers and to see Mary Stilwell.

On December 25, 1871, Thomas and Mary
married. They later had three children, Marion,
Thomas, Jr., and William.

Thomas loved his wife, but his work always came
first. Even on his wedding day he went to his shop to
work on an experiment.

Thomas Edison had odd work habits. He started work late and often fell asleep on his laboratory bench. He ate around midnight.

In 1876 Thomas moved to Menlo Park, New Jersey, and set up a large, two-story laboratory. His work led to many inventions. He became known as "The Wizard of Menlo Park."

In 1876 Alexander Graham Bell invented the
telephone. In 1877 Edison and his staff improved
it. They invented the carbon transmitter. It sent a
clearer sound and became part of the Bell telephone.

Then Thomas worked on a machine to save
sounds and replay them. In 1877 he invented
the phonograph.

In the 1870s homes were lit with candlelight and oil and gas lamps. But there were smoke, gas fumes, and the danger of fire. In 1878 Thomas Edison began searching for some way to use electricity to light homes.

Thomas Edison's notes filled hundreds of books. He said at the time, "I speak without exaggeration when I say that I have considered three thousand theories in connection with electric light."

He experimented for more than a year. "Genius," he said, "is one percent inspiration and ninety-nine percent perspiration."

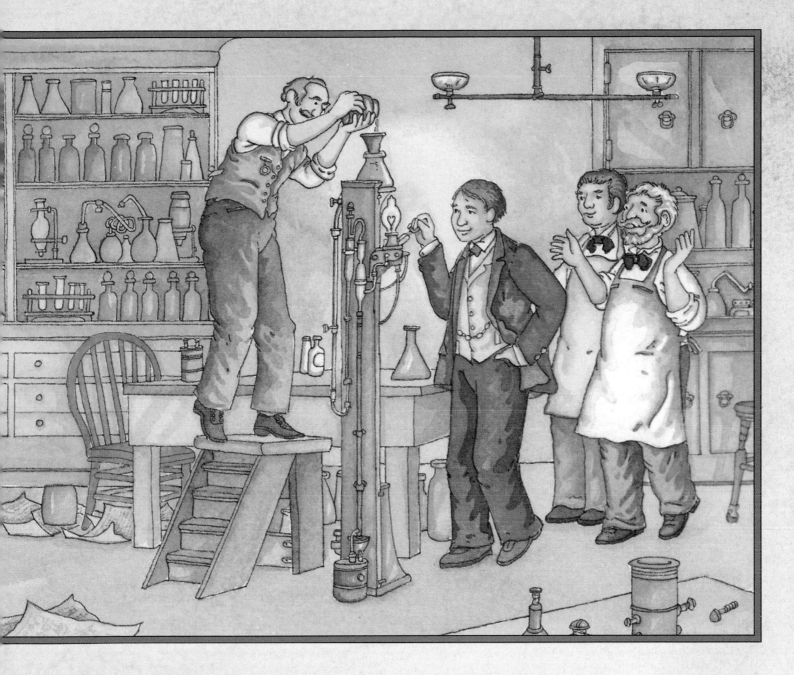

The electric light bulb he invented in 1879 had baked cotton thread inside. When electricity passed through the bulb, the thread glowed.

People came to Menlo Park to see Edison's new invention. And when they saw the lights, they wanted them in their homes. Thomas Edison hired workers to make bulbs, lamps, wires, and other things needed for this new form of light.

In 1882 in New York City he set up the Pearl
Street Station to generate electricity. In September
electricity was used to provide light for the first
eighty-five customers.

Edison's wife Mary had been ill for several years. Then, in July 1884, she contracted typhoid fever. She died on August 9, 1884. Following her death, Edison spent even more time with his work.

One evening the following year, while Thomas was visiting a friend in Boston, he met Mina Miller. She was a smart, well-educated woman. She was beautiful, too, with deep brown eyes and black hair. A few months later, while he was walking, he thought about Mina and was almost run over by a streetcar. Thomas Edison was in love.

Thomas married Mina on February 24, 1886. They moved to a large house in West Orange, New Jersey, and had three children together, Madeline, Charles, and Theodore.

Thomas developed a new phonograph with better sound. Then, in 1887, he placed a tiny phonograph inside a tin doll. With the turn of a crank, the doll seemed to talk.

Thomas Edison invented a movie camera and projector. In 1903 his company made the first movies to tell a story, *The Life of an American Fireman* and *The Great Train Robbery*.

He also invented the storage battery used in electric cars and submarines, a cement mixer, and a copying machine.

Thomas Alva Edison was issued 1,093 patents, more than any other inventor. He won many awards. In 1928 he was given the Congressional Medal of Honor for his many contributions to society.

In 1931 Thomas Edison said, "I am long on ideas but short on time." He had diabetes, stomach ulcers, and other ailments. He died on October 18, 1931, at the age of eighty-four.

To honor Thomas Edison, on the night of his funeral, lights all across the United States were turned off at ten o'clock.

Thomas Edison was an inventive genius. His inventions changed our world.

IMPORTANT DATES

1847	Born in Milan, Ohio, on February 11.
1854	The Edisons move to Port Huron, Michigan.
1863–1868	Worked as a telegraph operator in Canada and the United States.
1871	Married Mary Stilwell on December 25.
1874	Invented the quadruplex.
1877	Invented the carbon telephone transmitter and the first phonograph.
1879	Invented the electric light bulb.
1884	Wife Mary died on August 9.
1886	Married Mina Miller on February 24.
1891	Invented a motion picture camera.
1928	Awarded the Congressional Medal of Honor.
1931	Died in West Orange, New Jersey, on October 18.

CONTEST ENTRY

What's the Scoop?

AWARD WINNER

When Maura McCasted was a third grader, she entered a problem-solving contest sponsored by Invent America! Maura's invention not only won the contest, it solved a problem, too!

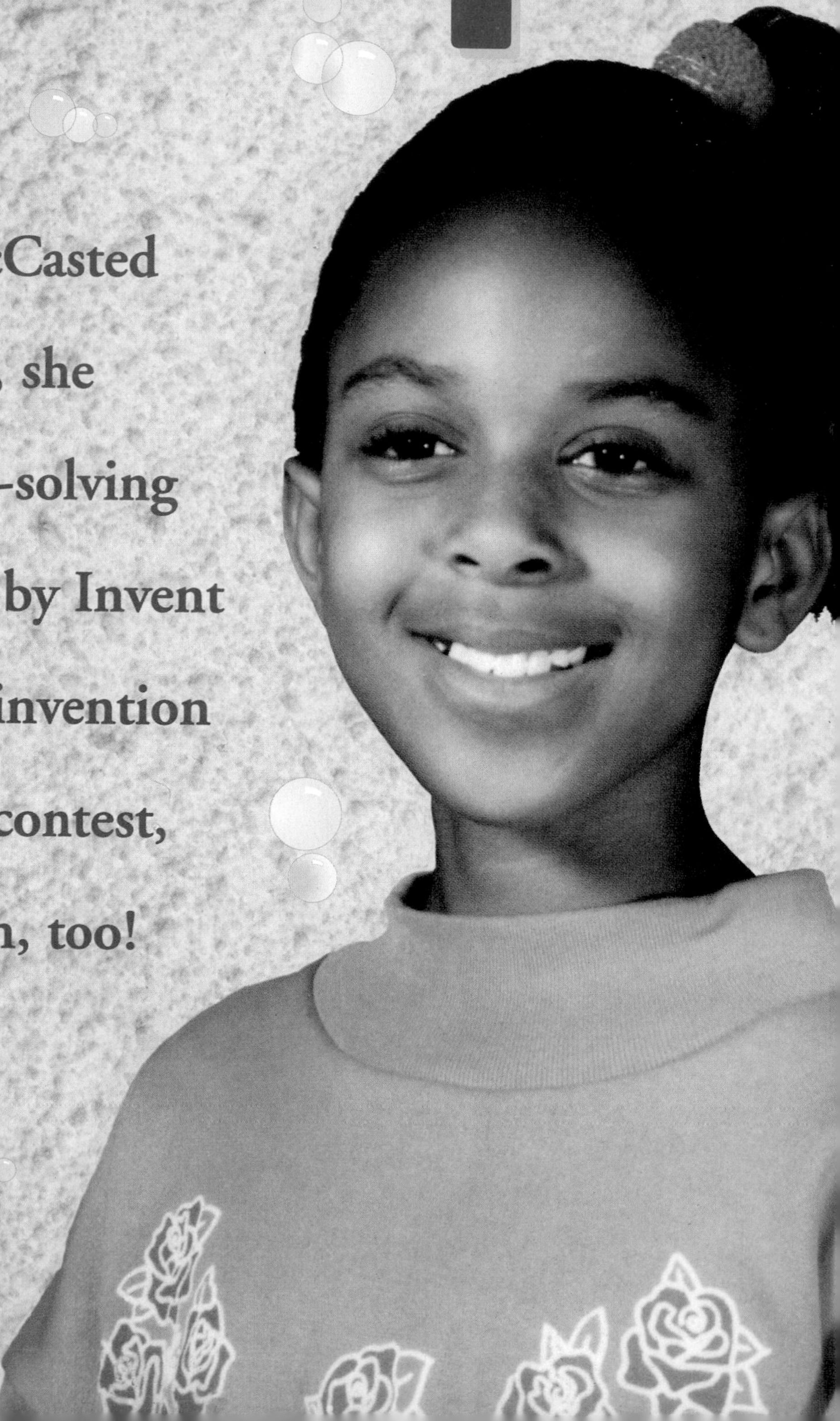

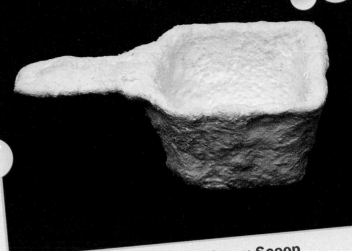

▲ Maura's Soap Savvy Scoop

STUDENT ENTRY FORM

Name Maura McCasted

My invention is called Soap Savvy

What is the need or problem solved?

I became aware as I was helping my mother wash the laundry, that a number of empty plastic detergent scoops were piling up on our laundry shelf. As a student supporting recycling in our community, I questioned why the plastic scoops were made from only 50% recycled materials. So, I invented a 100% Biodegradable Scoop for laundry detergent made out of compressed concentrated detergent itself!

How does your invention work?

My compressed concentrated detergent scoop works as well as any regular plastic scoop except, when your box of laundry detergent is empty you just throw in my Soap Savvy Scoop, and your last load of laundry will come clean and our environment will remain spotless.

How is your invention made?

I used a plastic laundry detergent scoop as my mold and put in a small amount of the actual detergent, fabric softener, and liquid soap and pressed it down with an identical scoop.

MY INVENTOR'S LOG

Date 10-6   Time 10:00 AM

First, I made a list of everyday problems. Then I chose my favorite problem, recycling plastic waste in the environment to keep our earth clean. To help do this I thought about inventing a laundry scoop that would completely dissolve.

Date 10-10   Time 1:00 PM

I went to three grocery stores with my mother to look at laundry scoops. After finding there were no scoops made from laundry detergent itself, I called the product information toll free phone number of a large soap company and they had none.

Date 10-13   Time 9:30 AM

I surveyed students at Stony Point North Elementary School and their teachers to see if my Soap Savvy idea was really new to them and if it would be useful, helpful, and affordable to buy. Everyone said they loved my idea and would buy it.

(Remember - neatness counts)   My Initials ___M.L.M.___

MY INVENTOR'S LOG

Date 10-14   **Time** 9:45 AM

I made my first detergent scoop out of a new ultra-concentrated detergent and a few drops of water. I pressed the mixture into a square plastic container and let it dry. It started to crumble when I tried to take it out.

Date 10-20   **Time** 9:45 AM

After applying the S.C.A.M.P.E.R. technique of problem solving to my invention, I designed another scoop made with a mixture of laundry detergent, fabric softener, and liquid soap. I pressed it down with another scoop. It worked much better.

Drawings or Photos

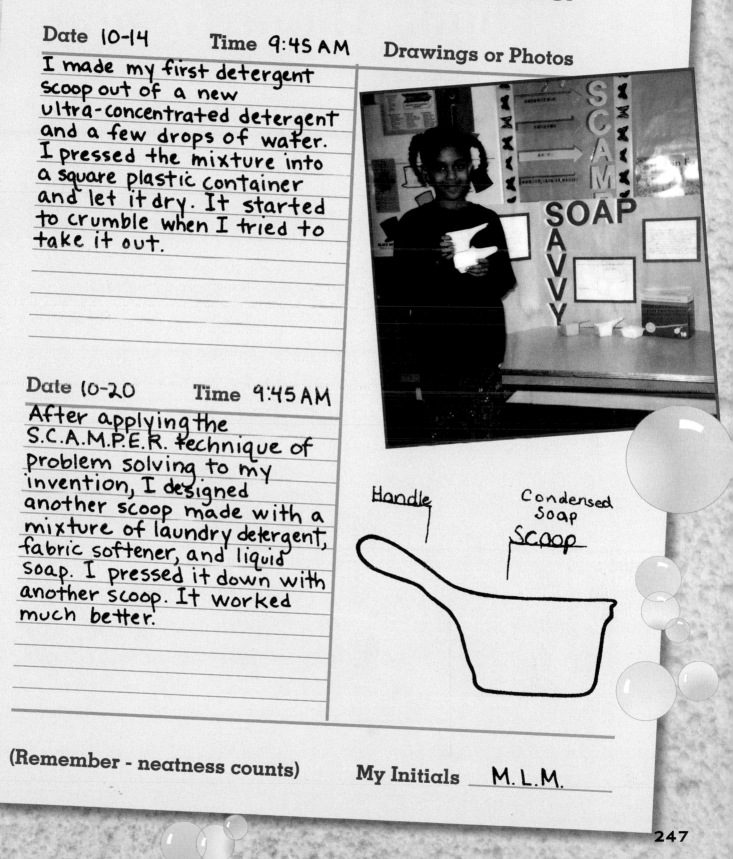

Handle

Condensed Soap

Scoop

(Remember - neatness counts)   **My Initials** _M.L.M._

Think About Reading

Write your answers.

1. What are three of Thomas Edison's inventions?

2. Think about Edison as a child. What clues tell you that he might grow up to be an inventor?

3. How do Thomas Edison's inventions make your life more pleasant?

4. Why do you think David A. Adler wrote a biography about Thomas Edison?

5. How are Maura McCasted and Thomas Edison alike?

Write a Newspaper Advertisement

Your job is to write an advertisement for Edison's light bulb. Your advertisement will be published in the *Menlo Park Gazette*. Before you write, list ways that the light bulb will make people's lives better. Your goal is to persuade people to buy electric light bulbs for their homes.

Literature Circle

Thomas Edison said, "Genius is one percent inspiration and ninety-nine percent perspiration." An inspiration is a great idea. "Perspiration" here means hard work. Talk about the meaning of this famous saying. Do you agree or disagree with it? Give reasons for your opinion.

Author
David A. Adler

What do George Washington, Rosa Parks, and Sitting Bull have in common? They are all subjects of biographies written by David A. Adler. He has also written children's mysteries, books about science, and humorous riddle books. Adler shares one important quality with Thomas Edison. He's curious about everything!

More Books by
David A. Adler

- *Amazing Magnets*
- *Calculator Riddles*
- *Cam Jansen and the Triceratops Pops Mystery*

How to
Draw a Floor Plan

Create a floor plan for a dream room.

Look around your classroom. Where are the windows and doors? Is there a closet or sink? About how many kids use the room? Architects need information like this when they make a floor plan. A floor plan is a diagram that shows the shape of a room. It also shows where windows, doors, and any built-in furniture should go.

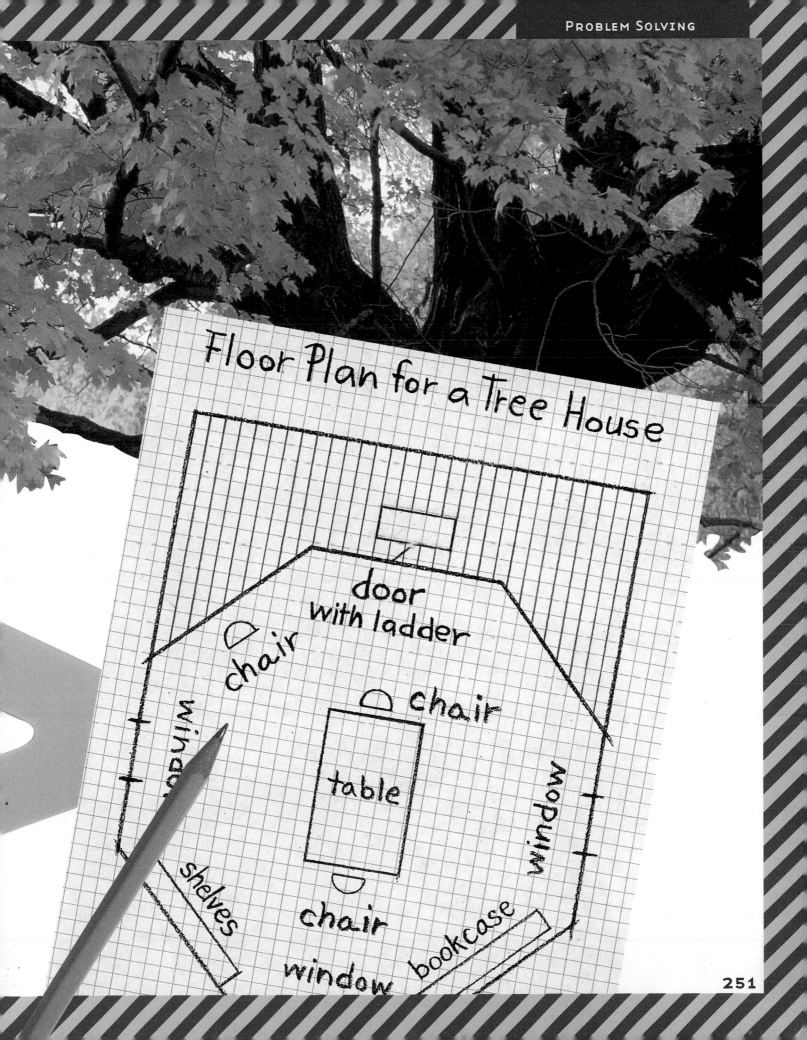

Floor Plan for a Tree House

door
with ladder

chair

chair

window

window

table

shelves

chair

bookcase

window

1

Choose a Room

Think of a room you would like to design. Maybe it's a room in a tree house or a library on a spaceship. Or maybe you want to improve a room that you use now. Jot down your ideas in your notebook. Then choose the one you like best.

Here are some places to find ideas:

- Look at the rooms in your home and at school. Write down what you like about them.

- Look at pictures of rooms in magazines and books.

- Think of rooms you've seen in movies and on TV.

TOOLS

- notebook

- plain paper, grid paper, and cardboard

- pencil

- ruler

- art supplies

2 Design a Room

You have chosen a room you want to design. Now the fun begins. Figure out what things the room needs to be comfortable, useful, or fun. For example, built-in shelves are a handy place to keep books and toys. A built-in table is a perfect place to draw and paint. Write down the things you will want to include in your floor plan.

These questions may help you:

- What shape is the room?
- How will I use it?
- How many doors and windows does it have?
- What features will make it special?

Now imagine how your room will look. Make some sketches of it. Show what you would see if you walked into the room.

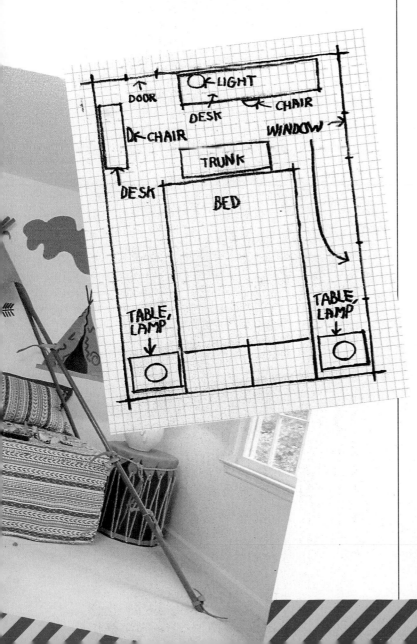

How Am I Doing?

Before you create your floor plan, take a minute to ask yourself these questions:

- Do I have a clear picture of what my dream room looks like?
- Will the room be comfortable and useful?
- Can I draw a floor plan with the information and ideas I have?

3 Draw a Floor Plan

Now you can make a floor plan of your dream room.

- First, draw an outline of the room's walls on grid paper.

- Next, draw in the windows and doors and label them.

- Then, draw and label any special features—built-in furniture, sinks, closets, and so on.

After you have finished your floor plan, write the title of your dream room at the top. Under the title, write "Designed by" and your name. Write a paragraph that tells how the room will be used and who will use it.

Tips
- Use a ruler to draw straight lines.
- If something on the **plan** doesn't look right, you can always **change it**.

4 **Show Your Floor Plan**

Display your design for a dream room. Tape your floor plan, drawings, and written description onto a large sheet of cardboard. Look at the room designs created by your classmates. How are they similar to yours? How are they different? Tell what you like about each design.

If You Are Using a Computer ...

Make your floor plan look professional by creating it on the computer. Use the line and shape tools to indicate what goes where, and label each item.

CONGRATULATIONS

You have discovered how to solve problems through careful planning. Now you can tackle all kinds of problems—big and small.

Jack Catlin
Architect ▶

ON THE JOB

THEME
Teams work best when they use each member's strengths to get the job done.

UNIT 3

Welcome to

LITERACY PLACE

Ad Agency

Teams work best when they use each member's strengths to get the job done.

THE STORY OF Z

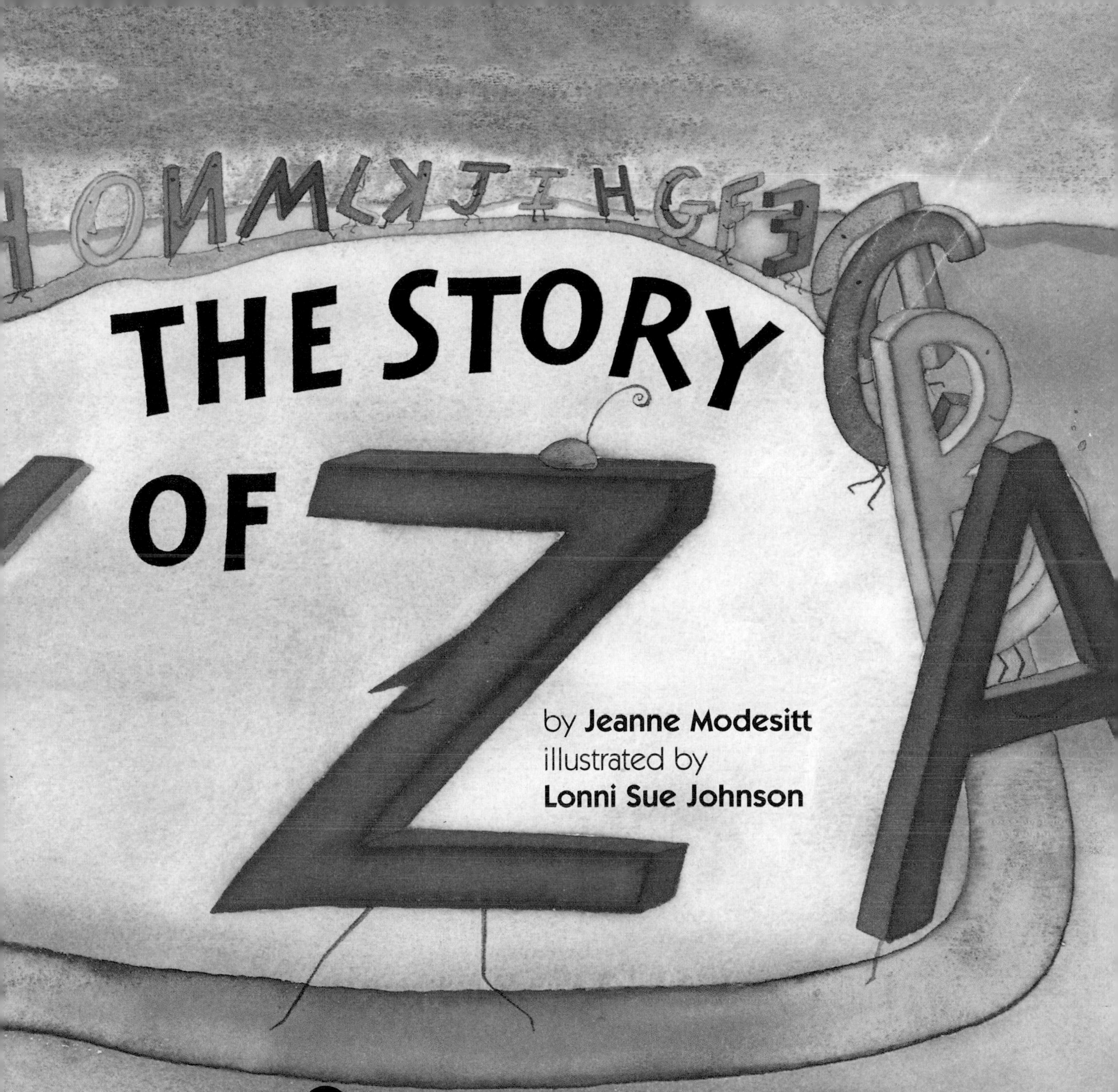

by **Jeanne Modesitt**
illustrated by
Lonni Sue Johnson

One day, the letter Z walked off the alphabet.
"I'm tired of being last in line," she had complained to
X and Y a few minutes earlier. "And my talents just seem
to go unnoticed. Why, I'll bet you I'm the least used
letter of the entire alphabet. It's enough to make
a letter want to leave."

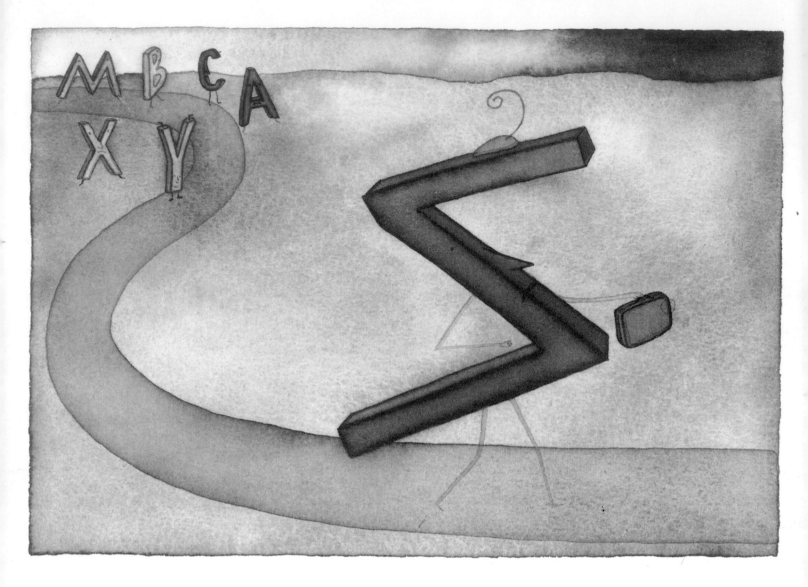

"Z!" gasped X. "How can you say such a thing? You can't leave the alphabet. To do so would be—"

"Mutiny!" cried Y. "Plain and simple mutiny!"

Z tossed her head at Y. "You're just upset because if I were gone, you'd be last in line."

She turned to X. "I've made up my mind. I'm going. Who knows? Maybe I'll start my own alphabet. Coming X?"

X dropped his eyes and said nothing.

"Very well," said Z. "I'm on my own." She sniffed loudly. "But I guess there's nothing new about **that**, is there?"

And off she went.

And the world was not the same without her.

For girls no longer understood boys when they pointed to the sky and said, "Did you see that plane ig-ag as it oomed by?"

Parents frowned at children when they begged, "Can
we go to the oo and see the ebras?"

And grandchildren laughed at grandparents when they reminded, "Don't forget to ip up your ippers."

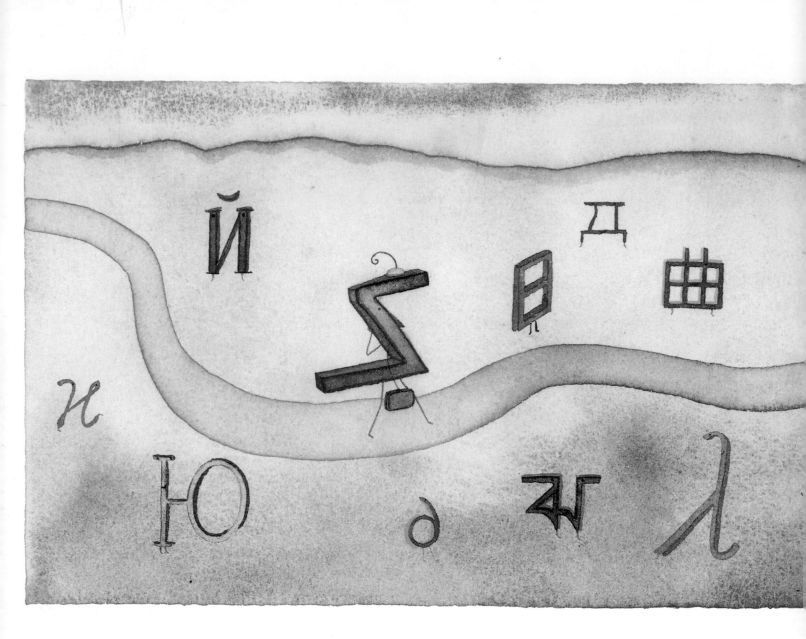

Needless to say, the moment Z left, almost everyone was crying out for her return. Even Y, the most conceited letter of the alphabet, admitted that things had run more smoothly before Z left.

And what did Z think of all this commotion? Well, she was too busy trying to start her own alphabet to even notice it.

But she wasn't having much luck. She couldn't convince any of the letters from the world's different alphabets to join her.

So she began to recruit other types of letters—letters
that had never belonged to an alphabet. Unfortunately,
such letters rarely do anything for anybody unless there's
something in it for them. In fact, the particular letters Z
came across were only interested in her idea of starting a
new alphabet because they thought the scheme might
make them a fast buck, and an easy one at that.

Of course, they didn't tell Z their hidden motives; they simply smiled and nodded and said, "Oh yes, yes, quite a noble plan."

Finally, after Z had made contact with fifteen of these so-called letters, she gathered them together and gave a quick pep talk on how they were about to become the greatest alphabet of all time—with her leading the way, of course.

But the minute she finished her speech and asked, "Now, who would like to be second?"—the letters began to push and shove and the whole thing turned into a brawl.

Z tried to stop the fight but was thrown up into the air, and landed nearby in a pile of leaves.

Moments later, the letters grew tired of fighting and took off in separate directions. Z was still sitting in the pile of leaves, wondering what to do next, when a street sweeper came along.

"Gad ooks!" he said, as he spotted half of Z sticking out from under the pile of leaves. "What have we here?"

Z looked at the sweeper with a frown. "Gad ooks," she repeated irritably. "What kind of word is that?"

"I'm sorry," said the man. "Let me try again. Gad ooks." Then the man began to cry. "You must forgive me," he said. "Life just hasn't been the same since Z left." The man kept on crying and took out a handkerchief.

"People say she was upset because she was last in line and wasn't used as often as the other letters." The man blew his nose. "I guess she didn't understand how important she was."

Z's attention perked. "Just as important as T?" she asked.

"Most certainly."

"As important as A or B or that silly Y?"

"Indeed yes."

Z stood up, throwing off her leaves.

"Z!" the man cried. He ran up and hugged her. "You're back. We've missed you so much. Please, please, won't you come home?"

Z thought for a moment and then dusted herself off. "Very well," she said. "I suppose I'd better. Can't have people running around saying gad ooks to one another."

And off she went . . .

273

to rejoin her alphabet.

And that night, for the first time in several weeks,

people could finally go to bed in peace.

Max Jerome

Art Director

Visit an advertising agency and meet the team!

What would you do if you made a sneaker that you wanted people to buy? What if you ran a cool new museum and you wanted kids to visit? What would you do? You might call an advertising agency. A special ad team there would find the best way to tell the world about your product.

PROFILE

Name: Max Jerome

Job: art director for an advertising agency

Hometown: New York City

Two words that describe you: funny, honest

Favorite team sport: football

Favorite comic strip: "Hagar the Horrible"

First jobs as a kid: newspaper boy, grocery store clerk

Tools that make your job easier: a computer and posterboard

 UESTIONS
for Max Jerome

Here's how art director Max Jerome creates advertisements you won't forget.

 Where did you grow up?

I was born in New York City. Then my family moved to Haiti. Later, we moved to Brooklyn, New York, where I spent most of my childhood.

What is your job?

I am an art director for an advertising agency. It's my job to make sure that the ads in magazines and on TV look good.

 Is that a hard job to do by yourself?

Oh, I couldn't do it alone. I work with a team of writers, designers, and artists. But I work most closely with one writer. It's important for me to work with someone who's good with words.

 Why are you and your writer a good team?

We trust each other. When we begin a new ad, we each come up with a bunch of dumb ideas. But that's okay, because we keep trying until we have an idea that we both like.

Q **What do you think makes a great ad?**

A A good ad makes people laugh and gets them to remember the product, too.

Q **What is your team's best ad campaign?**

A I think our best ad campaign was for the Liberty Science Center. This is a cool hands-on science museum in New Jersey. My team's job was to spread the news about this exciting place.

Q **How did you come up with exciting ads?**

A To get ideas, the writer and I went to the museum. We played in every exhibit—all 150 of them. Then we went back to the office and brainstormed. We wrote some headlines and drew lots of pictures until we had some great ideas for ads. The good news is that our ad ideas worked! Now the museum is really popular.

Q **When you were a kid, did you ever dream that you would end up in advertising?**

A Not really. But when I was a grocery store clerk, I loved reading cereal boxes. I liked looking at all the different designs. I guess that was a clue.

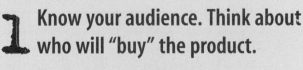

Max Jerome's Tips
for Creating an Ad

1 Know your audience. Think about who will "buy" the product.

2 Know where to put the ad. Think about where most people will see it.

3 Make it unusual. Think about what people will notice about the product.

"I played with bugs and didn't get yelled at."

Science Center

THINK ABOUT READING

Answer the questions in the story map.

CHARACTER

1. Who is the main character?

PROBLEM

2. What does Z do to upset the other characters? Why does she do this?

3. What big problem does Z's action cause?

EVENTS

4. What does Z try to do with other types of letters? What happens?

5. What happens when the street sweeper finds Z?

SOLUTION

6. What does Z do at the end of the story? Why?

WRITE A CHARACTER SKETCH

Write a character sketch about Z. Tell what kind of letter she really is! Think about her feelings and what she likes. What do her actions tell you about her? Be sure to include as many descriptive details as you can.

LITERATURE CIRCLE

Teamwork is important to the characters in *The Story of Z* and to mentor Max Jerome. Think of other books, movies, or TV programs in which the characters work together. Make a list. Then talk about the different kinds of teams. How are they alike? How are they different?

AUTHOR
Jeanne Modesitt

How does Jeanne Modesitt get ideas for her stories? She sees her ideas in her head. For her, story writing is like watching a short cartoon film. She likes to make kids laugh and wants to help them dream and hope. She says, "It's a wonderful job, writing for kids. I wouldn't change it for anything." Besides writing children's books, she gives workshops for young writers.

More Books by
Jeanne Modesitt

- *Lunch With Milly*
- *Sometimes I Feel Like a Mouse*

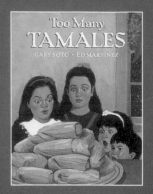

REALISTIC
FICTION

AWARD
WINNER

Too Many
TAMALES

by GARY SOTO

illustrated by ED MARTINEZ

Snow drifted through the streets and now that it was dusk, Christmas trees glittered in the windows.

Maria moved her nose off the glass and came back to the counter. She was acting grown-up now, helping her mother make *tamales*. Their hands were sticky with *masa*.

"That's very good," her mother said.

Maria happily kneaded the *masa*. She felt grown-up, wearing her mother's apron. Her mom had even let her wear lipstick and perfume. If only I could wear Mom's ring, she thought to herself.

Maria's mother had placed her diamond ring on the kitchen counter. Maria loved that ring. She loved how it sparkled, like their Christmas tree lights.

When her mother left the kitchen to answer the telephone, Maria couldn't help herself. She wiped her hands on the apron and looked back at the door.

"I'll wear the ring for just a minute," she said to herself.

The ring sparkled on her thumb.

Maria returned to kneading the *masa,* her hands pumping up and down. On her thumb the ring disappeared, then reappeared in the sticky glob of dough.

Her mother returned and took the bowl from her. "Go get your father for this part," she said.

Then the three of them began to spread *masa* onto corn husks. Maria's father helped by plopping a spoonful of meat in the center and folding the husk. He then placed them in a large pot on the stove.

They made twenty-four tamales as the windows grew white with delicious-smelling curls of steam.

A few hours later the family came over with armfuls of bright presents: her grandparents, her uncle and aunt, and her cousins Dolores, Teresa, and Danny.

Maria kissed everyone hello. Then she grabbed Dolores by the arm and took her upstairs to play, with the other cousins tagging along after them.

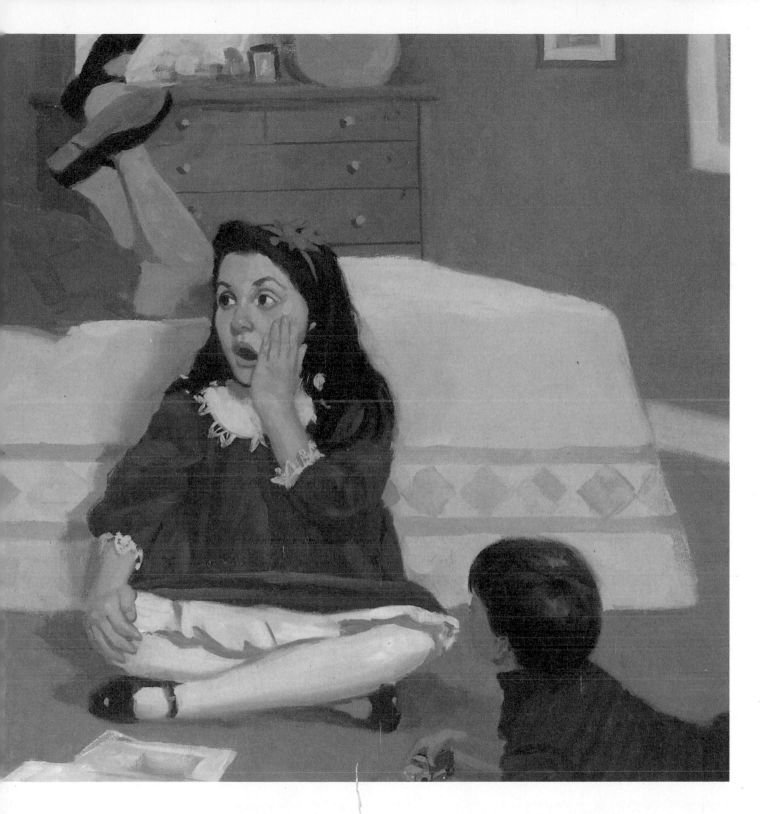

They cut out pictures from the newspaper, pictures of toys they were hoping were wrapped and sitting underneath the Christmas tree. As Maria was snipping out a picture of a pearl necklace, a shock spread through her body.

"The ring!" she screamed.

Everyone stared at her. "What ring?" Dolores asked.

Without answering, Maria ran to the kitchen.

The steaming tamales lay piled on a platter. The ring is inside one of the tamales, she thought to herself. It must have come off when I was kneading the *masa*.

Dolores, Teresa, and Danny skidded into the kitchen behind her.
"Help me!" Maria cried.
They looked at each other. Danny piped up first. "What do you want us to do?"

"Eat them," she said. "If you bite something hard, tell me."

The four of them started eating. They ripped off the husks and bit into them. The first one was good, the second one pretty good, but by the third tamale, they were tired of the taste.

"Keep eating," Maria scolded.

Corn husks littered the floor. Their stomachs were stretched till they hurt, but the cousins kept eating until only one tamale remained on the plate.

"This must be it," she said. "The ring must be in that one! We'll each take a bite. You first, Danny."

Danny was the youngest, so he didn't argue. He took a bite. Nothing.

Dolores took a bite. Nothing. Teresa took a big bite. Still nothing. It was Maria's turn. She took a deep breath and slowly, gently, bit into the last mouthful of tamale.

Nothing!

"Didn't any of you bite something hard?" Maria asked.

Danny frowned. "I think I swallowed something hard," he said.

"Swallowed it!" Maria cried, her eyes big with worry. She looked inside his mouth.

Teresa said, "I didn't bite into anything hard, but I think I'm sick." She held her stomach with both hands. Maria didn't dare look into Teresa's mouth!

She wanted to throw herself onto the floor and cry. The ring was now in her cousin's throat, or worse, his belly. How in the world could she tell her mother?

But I have to, she thought.

She could feel tears pressing to get out as she walked into the living room where the grown-ups sat talking.

They chattered so loudly that Maria didn't know how to interrupt. Finally she tugged on her mother's sleeve.

"What's the matter?" her mother asked. She took Maria's hand.

"I did something wrong," Maria sobbed.

"What?" her mother asked.

Maria thought about the beautiful ring that was now sitting inside Danny's belly, and got ready to confess.

Then she gasped. The ring was on her mother's finger, bright as ever.

"The ring!" Maria nearly screamed.

Maria's mother scraped off a flake of dried *masa.* "You were playing with it?" she said, smiling gently.

"I wanted to wear it," Maria said, looking down at the rug. Then she told them all about how they'd eaten the tamales.

Her mother moved the ring a little on her finger. It winked a silvery light. Maria looked up and Aunt Rosa winked at her, too.

"Well, it looks like we all have to cook up another batch of tamales," Rosa said cheerfully.

Maria held her full stomach as everyone filed into the kitchen, joking and laughing. At first she still felt like crying as she kneaded a great bowl of *masa,* next to Aunt Rosa. As she pumped her hands up and down, a leftover tear fell from her eyelashes into the bowl and for just a second rested on her finger, sparkling like a jewel.

Then Rosa nudged her with her elbow and said, "Hey, *niña,* it's not so bad. Everyone knows that the second batch of tamales always tastes better than the first, right?"

When Dolores, Teresa, and Danny heard that from the other side of the room they let off a groan the size of twenty-four tamales.

Then Maria couldn't help herself: She laughed. And pretty soon everyone else was laughing, including her mother. And when Maria put her hands back into the bowl of *masa,* the leftover tear was gone.

from

Laughing Tomatoes
Jitomates Risueños

poem by Francisco X. Alarcón
illustration by Maya Christina Gonzalez

Oda al maíz

padre
madre
regalo
del sol

tierra
agua
aire
luz

como
las razas
del mundo
te apareces

negro
amarillo
rojo
y blanco

tus elotes
nacen
apuntando
al cielo

tu pelo
de seda
lo mece
el viento

hermana
hermano
venado
verde

mis manos
cosecharán
tus sonrisas
enmascaradas

Ode to Corn

father
mother
gift from
the sun

earth
water
air
light

like
the races
of the world
you appear

black
yellow
red
and white

your tender ears
are born
pointing
to the sky

the wind
caresses
your silky
hair

sister
brother
green
deer

my hands
will harvest
your veiled
big smiles

WORLD'S ONLY CORN PALACE

MITCHELL CORN PALACE

1921

75th ANNIVERSARY

1892

In Praise of Corn

Welcome to Mitchell, South Dakota, home of the Corn Palace! Corn is Mitchell's biggest crop. It is also one of the most important crops in the world. All over the globe, people eat tortillas, tamales, bread, muffins, and cereals that are made from corn. In addition, millions of pigs and horses eat corn for breakfast, lunch, and dinner. Some of that corn is grown right here in Mitchell. We are so proud of our corn crop that we built the Corn Palace to honor it!

Concrete and Corn

The Corn Palace has stood in the heart of downtown Mitchell for over seventy-five years. The palace is built out of concrete, but its outside walls are made of corncobs. Each year, the face of the Corn Palace gets a new corncob design.

Oscar Howe, a Yanktonaise Sioux, designed the giant panels of the Corn Palace from 1948 to 1971.

Today's designer **Calvin Schultz** loved going to the Corn Palace as a boy. Little did he know he would one day grow up to design its murals.

Corncob Designs

The farmers of South Dakota don't grow only yellow corn. They grow red, blue, and white corn, too. All of these colored corns—as well as oats, barley, and other grains—go into the murals that cover the Corn Palace.

In early spring, Calvin Schultz begins by painting his new designs in miniature. Then, using chalk, he lays out his designs on black paper cut to the same size as the wall murals. Each section of the paper is numbered to show what color corn will go there— just like paint-by-numbers. The designs are cut out of the black paper. Last, the paper is tacked to the outside walls of the Corn Palace.

From Corn to Palace

By August, it is time to "paint with corn." Workers use power saws to cut thousands of ears of corn in half lengthwise. They then nail the flat side of the corn to the wood panels. Before long, the whole palace is covered with corn pictures.

In the fall, after the South Dakota corn crop has been harvested, the corn pictures are bold and beautiful. By winter, some ears of corn have been nibbled away. Birds and squirrels care little about the beauty of corn pictures. For them, the Corn Palace walls are a dream feast come true. That's all right.

By next August, brand new corn designs will appear on the walls of the Corn Palace. Tourists will pour out of cars and buses. They will point and snap pictures of the world's only Corn Palace.

THINK ABOUT READING

Write your answers.

1. Why do Maria and her cousins eat the tamales?

2. What is Maria's family like? How do the family members feel about each other?

3. Imagine that you are Maria. What would you do to find the ring?

4. How does Gary Soto show Mexican-American culture in this story?

5. Do you think Maria's family might like to visit the Corn Palace in Mitchell, South Dakota? Why?

WRITE A THANK-YOU NOTE

Imagine that you are Maria. You received a great present from one of your cousins at the family get-together. Write your cousin a thank-you note. Tell what you like about the gift. Be sure to include a date, a greeting, and a closing in your note.

LITERATURE CIRCLE

Did *Too Many Tamales* end the way you thought it would? Think of another happy ending for the story. Could the ring be someplace other than in the tamales? If so, what would happen? How would the characters feel? Would anything change in the beginning of the story? Make a flowchart to show what happens.

Author
Gary Soto

Gary Soto hasn't forgotten his childhood. In fact, his memories of growing up in a Mexican-American community in California often show up in his stories. He says, "Writing is my one talent. There are a lot of people who never discover what their talent is. I am very lucky to have found mine."

More Books by
Gary Soto

- *The Cat's Meow*
- *Chato's Kitchen*
- *Big Bushy Mustache*

How to

Design a Cereal Box

Think of all the kinds of cereal you see in the supermarket. There might be four brands of corn flakes alone! Why do you choose one brand and not another? Maybe the design of that cereal box catches your eye. The words and the colors on the box have been carefully chosen so that it "leaps off the shelf."

What is a design? A design is a plan or pattern for something. A cereal box design shows how the pictures and words appear on the box that the cereal comes in.

cereal's name written in large letters

colorful background

photograph makes the cereal look yummy

reasons to buy this cereal

1 Choose a Cereal

As a team, decide what kind of cereal you want to design a box for. To get started, you may want to list your team's favorite cereals. You can choose a real cereal or one that you make up.

TOOLS

- empty cereal box
- construction paper
- paper and pencils
- crayons, colored pencils, paints, scissors

2 Brainstorm Ideas

Bring in different kinds of empty cereal boxes from home. What do you notice about each one?

As a team, brainstorm ideas for the cereal box you'll design.

Tips
- The name should be easy to remember.
- Bright colors and large pictures get attention.

3 Create Your Cereal Box

As a team, decide what you want your cereal box to look like and what words you are going to use on it. Make a drawing that shows where the words and pictures will go. Next, cover an empty cereal box with construction paper. You're ready to add the design. Work together to make the finished cereal box.

4 Present Your Ideas

Cereal companies always test their designs. Your team can, too. Show your cereal box design to your classmates. Tell about the different features on your cereal box and why you chose them. Ask your classmates what they think of your design. Would they buy your cereal? Listen to the other teams' presentations. What good ideas did they have?

If You Are Using a Computer ...

Make your cereal box look professional. Type the words into your computer. Try different sizes and kinds of type. Print out what you've written. Then cut and paste.

THINK

Art directors often decide what the package a product comes in will look like. Why do you think they choose bright colors?

Max Jerome
Art Director ▶

FIRE!

IN YELLOWSTONE

by Robert Ekey

A bear and cub near Mystic Falls.
Most animals escaped the dangerous fires.

In 1988, spring came early in Yellowstone National Park. Snow that usually stays until June melted away under bright, sunny skies. Little rain fell.

The elk, moose, and grizzly bears grazed on an abundant supply of grass and other plants. Old Faithful geyser gushed as tourists snapped photographs. Yellowstone did not appear to be in a drought, but the forest was dry.

In June, a bolt of lightning struck a tree and started a small forest fire. Soon, lightning struck in other areas and started more fires in Yellowstone and on nearby forest lands. Each fire sent up a small column of smoke.

At first, park rangers allowed the fires to burn. Rangers had learned that fire has always been a vital part of the forest ecology, or the relationship between living things and their surroundings. Fire clears away old trees to make room for new plants and trees. Fires are as important to the growth of the forest as sunshine and rain.

This was not the first time Yellowstone had seen fires. Every year lightning starts fires. In fact, centuries ago, Native Americans used to light fires to drive game to hunters and to improve wildlife habitats.

Where Is Yellowstone?

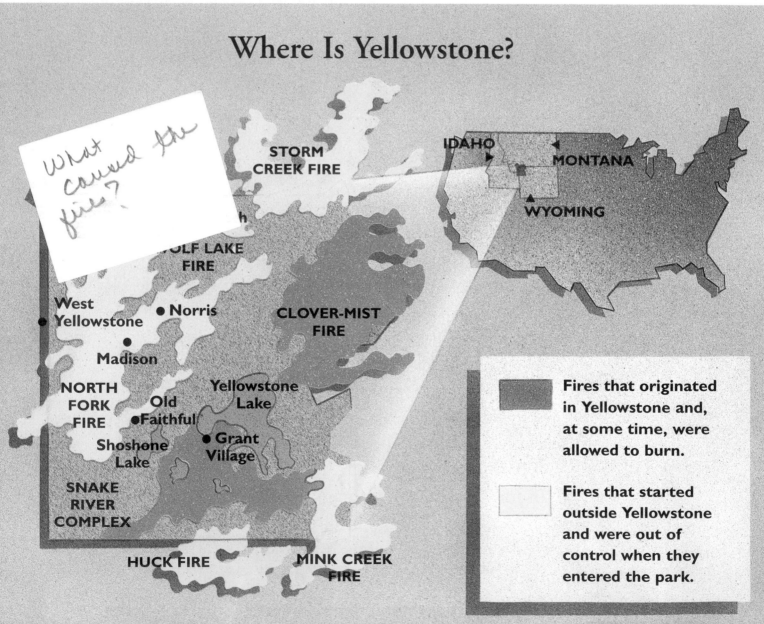

What caused the fire?

STORM CREEK FIRE

IDAHO

MONTANA

WYOMING

WOLF LAKE FIRE

West Yellowstone

Norris

CLOVER-MIST FIRE

Madison

NORTH FORK FIRE

Old Faithful

Yellowstone Lake

Shoshone Lake

Grant Village

SNAKE RIVER COMPLEX

HUCK FIRE

MINK CREEK FIRE

Fires that originated in Yellowstone and, at some time, were allowed to burn.

Fires that started outside Yellowstone and were out of control when they entered the park.

Most of the fires that start go out by themselves. Those that burn usually burn only a few acres. But 1988 was a different year. The heat of the summer and lack of rain left the forest very dry.

The fires in and near Yellowstone grew bigger. A careless woodcutter started another fire.

By the end of July, fires were close to buildings, and tourists moved from their campsites. Rangers decided they should try to put out all fires.

Most states sent firefighters to Yellowstone to battle the blazes. These young men and women fought hard to control the fires.

314

Bison calm in the midst of fires.
Elk and moose often entered burnt areas to eat.

But by August, the fires had continued to spread. No rain fell, and winds fanned the flames. Some days, the wind blew at gale force, spreading the fires over thousands of acres. Flames 200 feet tall swept through the forest faster than people can walk.

As the fires burned in the forest, the elk, bison, and other animals could easily escape the flames. Sometimes they were seen calmly grazing near the fires.

Many people who live near Yellowstone asked why rangers did not put out the fires. By then, the fires were too big. The worst drought in a century had left the forest too dry. The fires could not be stopped.

Clover-Mist fire at the foot of Pilot Peak.
It was a dangerous fire but beautiful at night.

Firefighting, modern and traditional: Firefighters used planes to take infrared maps of the land. They flew air tankers carrying water and chemicals that retard flames. They called in fire trucks from many stations. But to do this grueling work, they also had to use shovels, mules, and Pulaskis (a combination hoe and axe).

Thousands of firefighters were called to help, including soldiers from the U.S. Army and Marines. They used helicopters and airplanes to drop millions of gallons of water and chemicals on the fires. Firefighters used special tools to dig trails in the forest, in an attempt to stop the flames.

Every morning, smoke blanketed Yellowstone. Every afternoon, high winds blew, sending burning embers flying high in the sky. When the embers landed, they started more fires. Thousands of acres were on fire, and huge smoke columns filled the sky.

In early September—when the smoke column showed the fire was moving closer—tourists were still visiting Old Faithful. Firefighters sprayed buildings with water to keep them from burning.

Suddenly, the fire crested the ridge near Old Faithful! Rangers ordered tourists to leave quickly. A fierce firestorm swept across the parking lot near the old hotel there. It sent embers the size of golf balls skipping across the pavement.

The firestorm surprised firefighters. Many raced to help protect buildings and put out small fires started by the embers.

The fire at Old Faithful burned many trees and a few small cabins. But the larger buildings were saved, including the big old log hotel called the Old Faithful Inn. The fire seemed to pass as quickly as it came.

The next week, it started to rain and snow. It was the first rain in the park in weeks. The rain did what ten thousand firefighters could not do—it started to put the fires out.

The North Fork fire consumes one of the buildings of the Old Faithful complex. Flames devoured 16 buildings in all.

Inset: Firefighters wet the roof of the Norris Museum to protect it from embers.

By mid-September, nearly one million acres had burned in Yellowstone and 400 thousand in nearby forests. The area burned is the same size as the state of Delaware, but still less than half of the park was burned.

During the fires, many people argued that Yellowstone officials should have tried to put the fires out sooner. The officials answered that they could not have forecast the extreme drought conditions.

Only nature could stop what it started with the drought. "This is Mother Nature at work," one park ranger said. In the future, rangers decided, some fires will still be allowed to burn, but they will be watched more closely.

Left: Grass sprouts from the charred earth.

Middle: By spring, flowers are blooming and spreading through the forest.

Right: The heat of the fire caused lodgepole pine seeds to pop from their cones. They then rooted in the fertile ash and are now becoming a new forest.

Snow covered Yellowstone early in October. Early the next spring, the snow melted, providing water for the seeds and roots that had survived underground.

Where meadows had been burned, wildflowers bloomed in the spring and summer. In the forested areas, thousands of lodgepole pine seedlings sprouted as the forest was born again. None of the geysers was changed by the fire.

While fire forced some animals to move from the forest, it also provided new food sources for other wildlife. Biologists say that animals and plants adapt to fire. For some animals, fire even makes life easier.

Now, much rain has fallen, and the drought is over. Elk and bison graze on the new wildflowers and grasses. Birds sing in the trees. And tourists return to take pictures of the animals, the geysers, and the fresh young plants growing from the forest floor.

The Life Cycle of a Lodgepole Forest

Mature Forest   **Fire**   **0–60 Years**

60–150 Years   **150–300 Years**   **300–400 Years**

SMOKE JUMPER

Smoke jumper Margarita Phillips is well suited to fight a fire. Smoke jumpers put together and repair their own gear—except for their boots and helmets. The equipment Phillips jumps with weighs 85 pounds.

JUMPSUIT The heavily padded jumpsuit is made of the same material as bulletproof vests worn by police officers. Smoke jumpers wear fire-resistant clothing underneath.

RESERVE CHUTE
If the main parachute does not open, the reserve chute gets pulled into service.

PACK-OUT BAG
Tucked away in a jumpsuit, this bag is empty at first. Most fire fighting equipment is dropped to the ground in a separate container. Once a fire is out, a smoke jumper puts the equipment in the bag so it can be carried out.

MAIN PARACHUTE
Within five seconds of leaving the plane, a smoke jumper's parachute opens. It is carried inside a backpack.

STATIC LINE
A yellow nylon strap connects the main parachute to a cable inside the plane. The strap helps pull open the chute, which then disconnects.

HELMET
A motorcycle helmet has a protective metal face guard.

LEG POCKETS Inside go long johns and the "bird's nest"—looped nylon strap (shown on top of the pack-out bag) that smoke jumpers use to descend if they land in a tree. Also inside are signal streamers for communicating with the pilot from the ground.

CROSSCUT SAW Dropped to the ground in a cargo box, the saw is used to clear timber and branches from a fire line. Here the saw is bent over the pack-out bag and its teeth are covered.

Firefighter Raps It Up!

Firefighter Johnny Ruiz has a cool new way to teach fire safety tips to kids. He raps them. Here is one of Ruiz's raps.

Smoke Detectors

A **smoke detector**
  saves lives and property.

But like a brand new toy,
  it won't work
  without a **battery**.

A marvelous machine,
  it should be **tested**.

It's just like a firefighter
  who is **never rested**.

Firefighters know
  what detectors **can do**.

That's why I **rap**
  this message to you.

A detector's on duty,
  day and night.

Will it keep you **safe**?
  It just might!

THINK ABOUT READING

Write your answers.

1. Why did the Yellowstone forest burn so easily in 1988?

2. How did teamwork help to control the fire?

3. Do you agree with the way that Yellowstone officials handled the fire? Explain your answer.

4. How does the author show that forest fires can be both good and bad?

5. Imagine that Johnny Ruiz had been in Yellowstone Park during the fires. What are some jobs he might have done?

WRITE A DIARY ENTRY

Firefighters did tiring and dangerous work during the Yellowstone fire. Imagine you are one of these firefighters. Write a diary entry about one day during the summer of 1988. Be sure to describe what you saw, heard, and felt, as well as what you did.

LITERATURE CIRCLE

Suppose Yellowstone firefighters were giving a talk about fire prevention and safety. What tips might they include? What advice would they give campers in the forest? How would their safety pointers be different from Johnny Ruiz's tips?

AUTHOR
ROBERT EKEY

Robert Ekey knows all about the Yellowstone Park forest fires of 1988. He was there— writing about them! Every day he watched firefighters battle fierce blazes. He says, "Trying to stop the fires was like trying to stop a hurricane. Sometimes I had to run to escape the flames." Ekey wrote newspaper articles describing what he saw for *The Billings Gazette.* Today Ekey still lives close to Yellowstone and is happy to see that it has mostly recovered from the fires.

MORE BOOKS ABOUT
FIGHTING FIRES

- *Fire! Fire!* by Gail Gibbons
- *Flying Firefighters* by Gary Hines

The
Legend of the
Persian Carpet
TOMIE dePAOLA
ILLUSTRATED BY CLAIRE EWART

A WHITEBIRD BOOK

IRANIAN
FOLK TALE

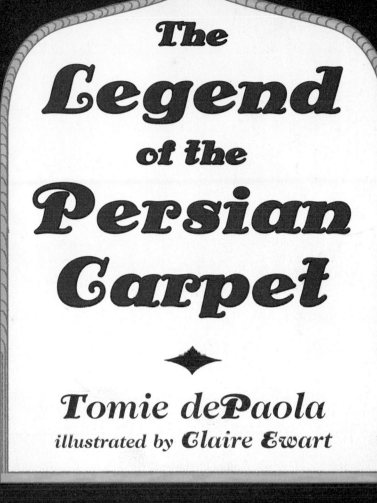

The Legend of the Persian Carpet

Tomie dePaola

illustrated by Claire Ewart

Many, many years ago, in the land once called Persia, there lived a kind and wise king, who was much loved by his people.

He lived in a white stone palace of many rooms, surrounded by gardens filled with flowers and fruit trees and sparkling fountains. King Balash had everything a man could desire.

But his most prized possession was a large diamond. This diamond was set on a special pedestal and was so beautiful and so bright that it filled not only the room it was in but all the surrounding rooms with a million rainbows.

King Balash was not a selfish man. He loved and
trusted his people so much that he kept no guards near
the diamond. Every afternoon, when the sun was just
right, and until it set, the king opened the doors of his
palace. Anyone who wished could come to see the walls
of the room painted with the diamond's light.

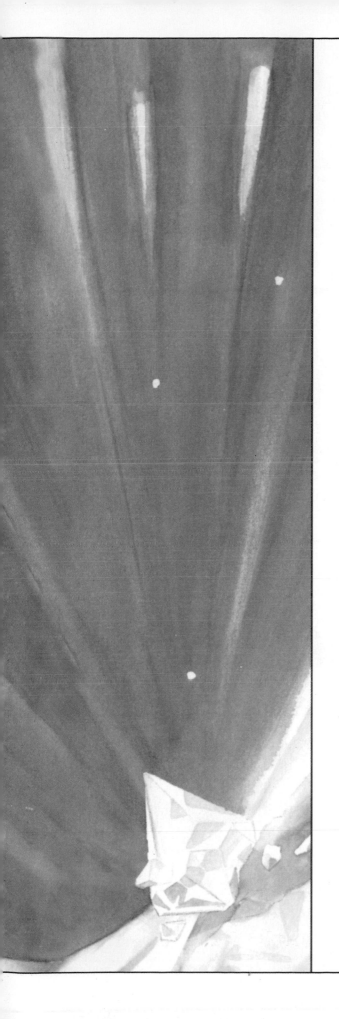

One day at dusk, as the crowds were leaving, a stranger to the kingdom slipped in among the visitors and stole the diamond. Like the wind, the thief raced his horse across the rocky plain toward the desert and the setting sun. But the horse stumbled, the diamond fell from the thief's hand, and it shattered on the rocks. The setting sun shone bloodred on the fragments and reflected a million sunsets into the thief's eyes. He staggered off empty-handed, cursing his luck and rubbing his eyes.

Now it was King Balash's custom to spend the time of the rising sun in the hall of the diamond with its amazing reflections. But instead of a million rainbows, all that greeted the king was the empty pedestal and a room filled with shadows and gloom.

"Call my people!" ordered the king. "I must
tell them of this tragedy. They must help me
find our treasure."

The people set out and soon a small boy named
Payam, who was an apprentice in the Street of
the Weavers, came to the rocky place. The morning
sun shot through the diamond fragments and
dazzled Payam with such a sight that he couldn't

believe his eyes. Off he ran to the palace and was
brought before the king.

"And there, O King," said Payam, "among all the
rocks, is the diamond, broken into a thousand pieces,
sparkling in the sun, reflecting all the colors of the
rainbow on the ground."

"I must see for myself," said the king. "Go
with me."

And when they reached the place, King Balash was so overwhelmed by the carpet of diamonds that he sat down and said, "I shall always stay here. I shall never enter the dark palace again."

"But Sire," cried Payam, "you can't! Who shall rule the kingdom? Who shall guide the people?"

But King Balash didn't listen. He stared at the shimmering light, lost in his own thoughts.

The people were all in confusion. Without a leader,

they and their homes could be attacked by any
robber-king from the desert. Their very lives were
in danger.

Payam sat and thought. He called all the other
young apprentices together.

"We must help our king and our people," Payam
told them. "We must make a carpet as miraculous as
the one our king stares at on the rocky plain. We must
all work together."

The apprentices agreed. And so did the master weavers and dyers of silk threads. Everyone set to work.

Payam went to King Balash.

"Please, Sire, come back and sit on the throne for a year and a day," Payam said. "If we cannot fill the room with color and light in that time, then we will accept our fate and live without a king. A year and a day."

It was the least he could do for his people. So King Balash agreed.

Day and night they all worked, spinning, dyeing, weaving on the large rug loom. And in a year and a day, the carpet was finished.

339

The workers carried the carpet
to the palace and into the dark hall
where the diamond had rested. With
a flourish, they unrolled it before
the king.

Suddenly the room was once
more filled with the colors of the
rainbow. Reds, golds, blues, and
greens of the silk carpet glowed on
the floor, reflecting color off the
walls and the ceiling. Once more, the
room was filled with light and King
Balash and his people were happy.

And happiest of all were Payam
and the other apprentices, for they
had not only saved their kingdom,
but had made the most beautiful
carpet in the world.

High-Tech Carpet

Did you see the movie *Aladdin*? If you did, you know that it's possible to make a carpet fly, creep, and even show feelings—in a movie, at least. Meet the team that used paint, paper, and a computer to make a rug that does much more than lie on a floor!

THE ANIMATOR

Randy Cartwright was the head animator of the team. His job was to do all the drawings of the Magic Carpet. Cartwright had to turn a rug into a movie character. It had to have a winning personality, no less. How did Cartwright do it?

First, Cartwright took a piece of cloth and pretended it was the carpet. He folded the cloth in lots of different ways to see if he could make it look happy, sad, or excited. What a challenge!

Next, Cartwright made some drawings. In one, he drew a fold at the top of the carpet. It looked a little like a head. That was a start. Then, he had the idea of making the tassels seem to be hands and feet. He drew the carpet's "hand" holding its "stomach." Success! The Magic Carpet looked like it was having a good laugh.

© Disney Enterprises, Inc

Randy Cartwright flips through drawings so he can see how the carpet looks when it moves.

Believe it or not, a carpet can show many different feelings.

Laughing

Dreamy

Thoughtful

343

© Disney Enterprises, Inc

© Disney Enterprises, Inc

Richard Vander Wende made up the Magic Carpet's fancy pattern.

THE ARTIST

Now that the Magic Carpet had a sense of humor, it needed a design, too. So artist Richard Vander Wende created a beautiful one. It included colorful tigers' heads, swords, lamps, and flames.

The next step was to paint the design on every single one of Cartwright's drawings of the carpet. In most cartoons, artists paint everything by hand. Painting Vander Wende's complicated design on hundreds of thousands of drawings would have taken forever. Fortunately, there was another way.

Excited

Curious

Shocked

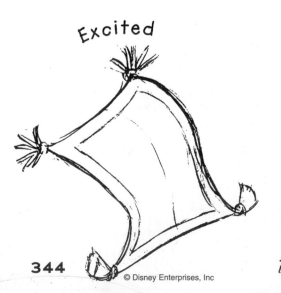

THE COMPUTER ANIMATOR

Tina Price came to the rescue. She's a computer animator. Her computer has a special program that allows her to create cartoon characters.

First, Price copied Cartwright's black-and-white drawings of the Magic Carpet into her computer. Next, she entered Vander Wende's design into her computer. Then, almost before you could say *Abracadabra*, she "zapped" the colorful design on each computer drawing.

The completed drawings of the Magic Carpet were filmed and added to the other scenes in the movie. By the time the team was finished, Aladdin's Magic Carpet was rolling up with laughter!

The Magic Carpet is ready for its starring role.

Think About Reading

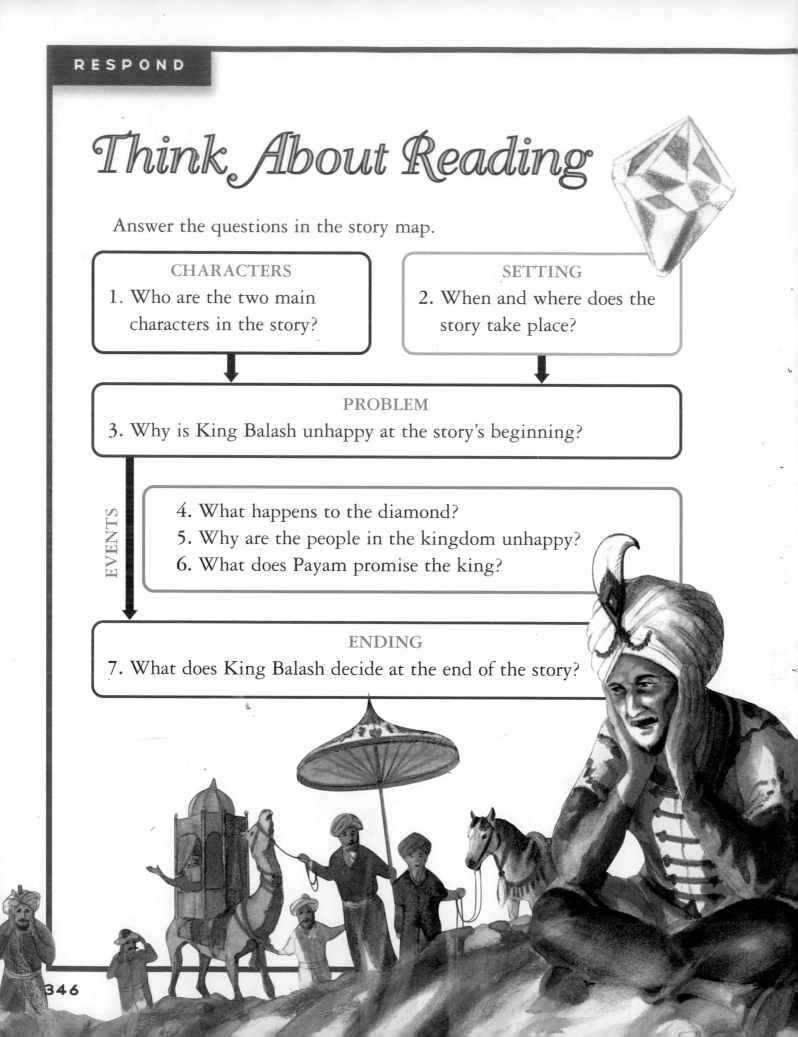

Answer the questions in the story map.

CHARACTERS

1. Who are the two main characters in the story?

SETTING

2. When and where does the story take place?

PROBLEM

3. Why is King Balash unhappy at the story's beginning?

EVENTS

4. What happens to the diamond?
5. Why are the people in the kingdom unhappy?
6. What does Payam promise the king?

ENDING

7. What does King Balash decide at the end of the story?

Write a Poem

Write an acrostic poem. On a sheet of paper, write the word *carpet* going down the page like this.

C
A
R
P
E
T

Next to each letter, write a describing word or phrase that begins with that letter. If you close your eyes and picture the carpet's colors, design, and size, you'll get lots of ideas. For example, for **C** you might write "colorful" or "clever design."

Literature Circle

Think of the carpet in the movie *Aladdin*. How is it made? What kind of team makes it? How is Aladdin's carpet different from King Balash's carpet? How is it the same? Record your ideas on a chart.

Author
Tomie dePaola

Tomie dePaola is bursting with ideas. To prove it, he has written over 200 books for children. *The Legend of the Persian Carpet* is the first one that he has not illustrated himself. He says, "I do a lot of writing in my head first, just thinking the story through." He revises each book many times until he gets it just right. Tomie dePaola has written all kinds of books, but he's especially fond of folk tales.

More Books by
Tomie dePaola

- *The Legend of the Bluebonnet: An Old Tale of Texas*
- *Strega Nona Meets Her Match*

How to
Write a Slogan

Can you think of a short, catchy sentence or phrase that you've heard on the radio or TV? Is there a clever saying about recycling or picking up litter that you say over and over again? It's probably a slogan for a particular product or service.

What is a slogan? A slogan is a phrase or sentence that helps sell a product, a service, or an idea. Slogans are a popular and fun way to advertise. And they're easy to remember!

BOOKS FOR

BE COOL.

A public service slogan sells an idea instead of a product.

EVERYONE

EVERYONE FOR BOOKS

•DIANE GOODE•

STAY IN SCHOOL.

Slogans can give an order that grabs your attention.

Slogans can rhyme.

1 What's It About?

With your team, choose a product, service, or idea to create a slogan for. Choose something that you really like or believe in. It could be a favorite food, a new video game, a reminder to recycle, or an upcoming school event. Make a list of your choices. Decide which one you'd like to create a slogan for.

TOOLS

• paper and pencil

2 Brainstorm Ideas

Slogans are everywhere. List some slogans that you and your teammates remember from television and radio ads, posters, or newspapers and magazines. Talk about the slogans with your team. Which ones do you like the most? Why? What makes the slogans easy to remember?

3 Write Your Slogan

Use what you have learned about slogans to create one of your own. These questions may help you.

- What is the best thing about your product, service, or idea?
- What are some fun words that describe the product?

Tips
- Short slogans are easy to remember.
- Rhyming slogans stick in people's minds.
- Using words that start with the same letter can make a slogan sound good.

4 Test Your Slogan

Share your team's slogan with your classmates. Find out if they think your slogan is catchy. Will it encourage them to like your idea, use your service, or buy your product? Listen to the slogans other teams made up. What makes their slogans successful?

If You Are Using a Computer ...

Try printing your slogan in the Banner or Sign format. Use clip art to decorate your work.

THINK

Ad teams use slogans to help people remember products. Which kinds of slogans do you remember best?

Max Jerome
Art Director ▶

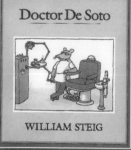

Doctor De Soto

by WILLIAM STEIG

Doctor De Soto, the dentist, did very good
work, so he had no end of patients. Those close to his
own size—moles, chipmunks, et cetera—sat in the regular
dentist's chair.

Larger animals sat on the floor, while Doctor De Soto
stood on a ladder.

For extra-large animals, he had a special room. There
Doctor De Soto was hoisted up to the patient's mouth by
his assistant, who also happened to be his wife.

Doctor De Soto was especially popular with the big animals. He was able to work inside their mouths, wearing rubbers to keep his feet dry; and his fingers were so delicate, and his drill so dainty, they could hardly feel any pain.

Being a mouse, he refused to treat animals dangerous to mice, and it said so on his sign. When the doorbell rang, he and his wife would look out the window. They wouldn't admit even the most timid-looking cat.

One day, when they looked out, they saw a well-dressed fox with a flannel bandage around his jaw.

"I cannot treat you, sir!" Doctor De Soto shouted. "Sir! Haven't you read my sign?"

"Please!" the fox wailed. "Have mercy, I'm suffering!" And he wept so bitterly it was pitiful to see.

"Just a moment," said Doctor De Soto. "That poor fox," he whispered to his wife. "What shall we do?"

"Let's risk it," said Mrs. De Soto. She pressed the buzzer and let the fox in.

He was up the stairs in a flash. "Bless your little hearts,"
he cried, falling to his knees. "I beg you, *do* something!
My tooth is killing me."

"Sit on the floor, sir," said Doctor De Soto, "and remove
the bandage, please."

Doctor De Soto climbed up the ladder and bravely
entered the fox's mouth. "Ooo-wow!" he gasped. The fox
had a rotten bicuspid and unusually bad breath.

"This tooth will have to come out," Doctor De Soto
announced. "But we can make you a new one."

"Just stop the pain," whimpered the fox, wiping some tears away.

Despite his misery, he realized he had a tasty little morsel in his mouth, and his jaw began to quiver. "Keep open!" yelled Doctor De Soto. "Wide open!" yelled his wife.

"I'm giving you gas now," said Doctor De Soto. "You won't feel a thing when I yank that tooth."

Soon the fox was in dreamland. "M-m-m, yummy," he mumbled. "How I love them raw . . . with just a pinch of salt."

They could guess what he was dreaming about. Mrs. De Soto handed her husband a pole to keep the fox's mouth open.

Doctor De Soto fastened his extractor to the bad tooth. Then he and his wife began turning the winch. Finally, with a sucking sound, the tooth popped out and hung swaying in the air.

"I'm bleeding!" the fox yelped when he came to.

Doctor De Soto ran up the ladder and stuffed some gauze in the hole. "The worst is over," he said. "I'll have your new tooth ready tomorrow. Be here at eleven sharp."

The fox, still woozy, said goodbye and left. On his way home, he wondered if it would be shabby of him to eat the De Sotos when the job was done.

After office hours, Mrs. De Soto molded a tooth of pure gold and polished it. "Raw with salt, indeed," muttered Doctor De Soto. "How foolish to trust a fox!"

"He didn't know what he was saying," said Mrs. De Soto. "Why should he harm us? We're helping him."

"Because he's a fox!" said Doctor De Soto. "They're wicked, wicked creatures."

That night the De Sotos lay awake worrying. "Should we let him in tomorrow?" Mrs. De Soto wondered.

"Once I start a job," said the dentist firmly, "I finish it. My father was the same way."

"But we must do something to protect ourselves," said his wife. They talked and talked until they formed a plan. "I think it will work," said Doctor De Soto. A minute later he was snoring.

The next morning, promptly at eleven, a very cheerful fox turned up. He was feeling not a particle of pain.

When Doctor De Soto got into his mouth, he snapped it shut for a moment, then opened wide and laughed. "Just a joke!" he chortled.

"Be serious," said the dentist sharply. "We have work to do." His wife was lugging the heavy tooth up the ladder.

"Oh, I love it!" exclaimed the fox. "It's just beautiful."

Doctor De Soto set the gold tooth in its socket and hooked it up to the teeth on both sides.

The fox caressed the new tooth with his tongue.

"My, it feels good," he thought. "I really shouldn't eat them. On the other hand, how can I resist?"

"We're not finished," said Doctor De Soto, holding up a large jug. "I have here a remarkable preparation developed only recently by my wife and me. With just one application, you can be rid of toothaches forever. How would you like to be the first one to receive this unique treatment?"

"I certainly would!" the fox declared. "I'd be honored." He hated any kind of personal pain.

"You will never have to see us again," said Doctor De Soto.

"*No one* will see you again," said the fox to himself. He had definitely made up his mind to eat them—with the help of his brand-new tooth.

Doctor De Soto stepped into the fox's mouth with a bucket of secret formula and proceeded to paint each tooth. He hummed as he worked. Mrs. De Soto stood by on the ladder, pointing out spots he had missed. The fox looked very happy.

When the dentist was done, he stepped out. "Now close your jaws tight," he said, "and keep them closed for a full minute." The fox did as he was told. Then he tried to open his mouth—but his teeth were stuck together!

"Ah, excuse me, I should have mentioned," said Doctor De Soto, "you won't be able to open your mouth for a day or two. The secret formula must first permeate the dentine. But don't worry. No pain ever again!"

The fox was stunned. He stared at Doctor De Soto, then at his wife. They smiled, and waited. All he could do was say, "Frank oo berry mush" through his clenched teeth, and get up and leave. He tried to do so with dignity.

Then he stumbled down the stairs in a daze.

Doctor De Soto and his assistant had outfoxed the fox. They kissed each other and took the rest of the day off.

from *Amazing Mammals*

The Fox

written by Alexandra Parsons photographed by Jerry Young

Foxes are members of the dog family. They sleep all day in underground burrows and come out at night to search the woods and fields for food.

Secret stores

Foxes don't hunt for food only when they are hungry. Sometimes they hide food in a secret place in case they get hungry later.

The mouse leap

Mice are tricky to catch. The clever fox sneaks up softly. Then it jumps up high and dives down right on top of its prey.

Foxed!

Foxes are famous for their cunning. An old story tells how a fox tricks a crow into dropping a piece of cheese. The fox flatters the crow and asks it to sing. When the vain bird opens its beak, out pops the cheese.

A fox's ears are so sensitive it can hear a worm wriggling on the other side of a field.

Mmm, tasty!

Foxes eat just about anything, from worms to chickens. Some even sneak into town and raid trash cans.

Arctic fox

Not all foxes are red. One kind of fox lives in the Arctic, where its white winter coat is a perfect disguise in the snow.

Family life

A mother fox gives birth to around five little cubs at one time. She looks after them while the father fox goes out to search for food. Both the mother and the father teach their cubs to hunt and fight by playing games with them.

Foxy sounds

Foxes yap, howl, bark, and whimper, just like dogs do.

Think About Reading

Write your answers.

1. What does Doctor De Soto do for the fox?

2. Why do Doctor and Mrs. De Soto decide to help the fox?

3. Doctor De Soto says that foxes are "wicked, wicked creatures." Is Doctor De Soto right? Why or why not?

4. How do William Steig's illustrations help you to understand and enjoy the story?

5. What kind of characters are Doctor De Soto and his wife? How do you know?

Write an Advertising Poster

Doctor De Soto wants to advertise his dental practice. Write a poster that tells what a good dentist he is. Be sure to describe the special treatment he gives his patients. You may even wish to quote one or two happy animals. Then illustrate your poster and display it in the classroom.

Literature Circle

Suppose the fox told the story about having his tooth fixed by the De Sotos. How would the story change? How would the ending change? Which ending do you like better—the real one or the one you just made up?

Author
William Steig

William Steig was 60 years old when he wrote his first children's book. Since then he has won many awards. He likes to use long, outrageous words in his clever stories because he thinks that young readers are intelligent. Steig says, "Writing is fun. I really enjoy that. I think writing's a good career."

More Books by
William Steig
- *Abel's Island*
- *Amos & Boris*
- *CDB!*

How to
Create an Ad Campaign

Work with your team to plan all kinds of ads.

How does a company tell the world about a new product or service? One way is to create an advertising, or ad, campaign. An ad campaign can include TV and radio commercials, ads in magazines, billboards, bumper stickers, and even T-shirts! Who thinks of all these different kinds of ads? A special team of writers and artists at an ad agency does. Each team member brings special skills and knowledge to an ad campaign.

Research a Product

With your team, choose a product, a service, or a fun place to go—like a park or museum—for your ad campaign. Pick something that team members like and know about. Next, ask yourselves, "What's so great about this product?" Brainstorm and list reasons that people should use it.

Think of things that make your product better than others of its kind. Do some market research. Ask people you know what they like about your product. This will help you decide how to advertise it.

Your team may want to create a public-service ad campaign. Public-service ads present useful information. They may tell about staying healthy and safe, taking care of nature, or even recycling.

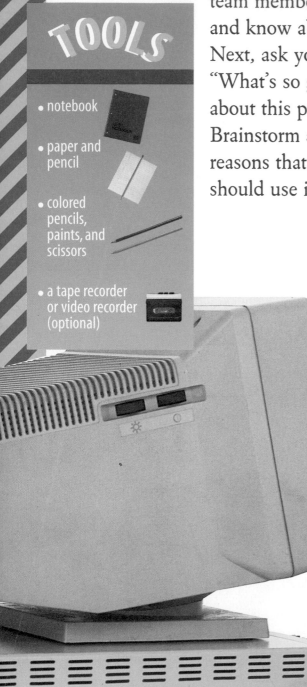

TOOLS

- notebook
- paper and pencil
- colored pencils, paints, and scissors
- a tape recorder or video recorder (optional)

2

Do Your Part

As a group, decide which kinds of ads to create for your campaign. Then, as a team, decide what each member will do. The jobs might include: writing magazine and newspaper ads; creating radio and TV scripts; making up jingles or songs about the product; thinking of a slogan; and designing posters, buttons, billboards, hats, or T-shirts.

Before you begin the ad campaign, look at and listen to lots of ads to get ideas. Share what you find with your team.

How Am I Doing?

Before your team begins to create an ad campaign, ask yourselves these questions.

- Have we chosen a product that all team members agree on?

- Have we brainstormed ideas about why people would want to buy this product?

- Have we asked others what they think about this product?

Tip Keep your ads simple. The fewer the words, the easier they will be to remember.

↑ I like the hurdle idea.

This one works better in black and white.

Try using different colors.

Start the Campaign

Create ads for your campaign. Make them fun and lively. If you are making a radio or TV commercial, you might want to tape it. As a team, look at all the ads you created. Are they exciting and colorful? Will the ads make people want to buy the product? Make any changes your group decides on. Now your campaign is ready to go.

Stay on Track

Snazzy Sneakers

1st Place

4 Present Your Ads

As a team, present your ads to the class. Team members can show the parts of the campaign they worked on. Ask your classmates how they feel about your product. Look at other teams' presentations.

What good ideas did they have? What kinds of products and ads did they choose? Discuss how working together helped create successful ad campaigns.

If You Are Using a Computer...

Use your computer to design magazine and newspaper ads with the Sign format. Try different kinds and sizes of type and clip art, too. Then print out your exciting new ads. You can also type your advertising slogans in the Banner format to print out and hang up in the classroom.

CONGRATULATIONS

Now you know what it's like to get a job done—and to work on a team. Look around you. What other jobs are done by teams?

Max Jerome
Art Director ▶

You will find all your vocabulary words in alphabetical order in the Glossary. Look at the sample entry below to see how to use it.

This is the **entry word** you look up. It is divided into syllables.

This part tells you how to **pronounce** the entry word. It uses the marks in the pronunciation key.

This tells you what **part of speech** the entry word is.

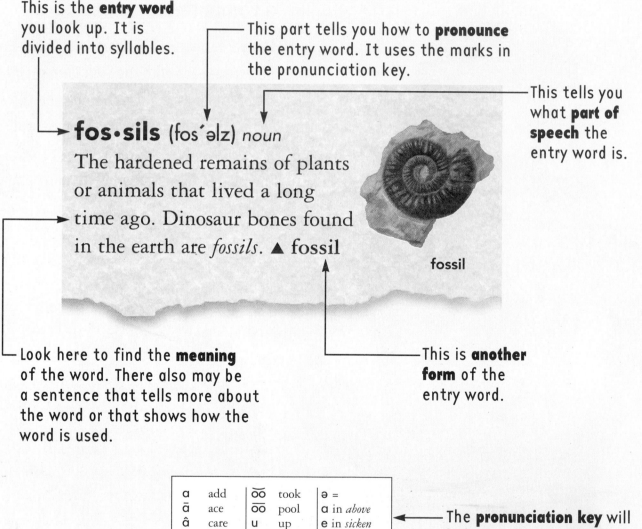

fos·sils (fos′əlz) *noun*
The hardened remains of plants or animals that lived a long time ago. Dinosaur bones found in the earth are *fossils*. ▲ fossil

fossil

Look here to find the **meaning** of the word. There also may be a sentence that tells more about the word or that shows how the word is used.

This is **another form** of the entry word.

a	add	o͝o	took	ə =	
ā	ace	o͞o	pool	a in *above*	
â	care	u	up	e in *sicken*	
ä	palm	û	burn	i in *possible*	
e	end	yo͞o	fuse	o in *melon*	
ē	equal	oi	oil	u in *circus*	
i	it	ou	pout		
ī	ice	ng	ring		
o	odd	th	thin		
ō	open	th	this		
ô	order	zh	vision		

The **pronunciation key** will help you figure out how to pronounce the entry word.

ap·pren·tic·es
(ə pren´ ti siz) *noun*
People who learn a trade
or job by working with a
more skilled person.
▲ apprentice

bed·rock
(bed´ rok´) *noun*
The solid layer of rock
that lies under the soil
and loose rock.

bel·lowed
(bel´ ōd) *verb*
Shouted or roared. I
bellowed when my dog
ate my sandwich.
▲ bellow

bi·cus·pid
(bī kus´ pid) *noun*
A tooth with two points
on its top.

blaz·es (blā´ ziz) *noun*
Large fires. ▲ blaze

bri·dles (brīd´ lz) *noun*
The straps, bits, and
reins that fit over horses'
heads and are used to
guide the animals.
▲ bridle

buf·fa·loes
(buf´ ə lōz´) *noun*
Wild oxen of North
America that have large,
shaggy heads. Buffalo
are also called bison.
▲ buffalo

buffaloes

cal·lig·ra·phy
(kə lig´ rə fē) *noun*
Fancy penmanship,
or a kind of
beautiful writing.

calligraphy

chaps
(chaps or shaps) *noun*
Leather leg coverings
that are worn over pants.
Chaps are worn by
cowhands to protect
their legs from thorns.

chick·en·pox
(chik´ ən poks´) *noun*
A childhood disease that
causes red, itchy bumps
on the skin.

379

chop·sticks
(chop´ stiks´) *noun*
A pair of thin sticks used to lift food to the mouth. Chopsticks are used mostly in Asian countries. ▲ **chopstick**

chopsticks

coaxed (kōkst) *verb*
Encouraged someone gently to do something. We *coaxed* our friend to stay for lunch. ▲ **coax**

col·umns
(kol´ əmz) *noun*
Things having the shape of tall, upright structures that support a building. *Columns* of smoke rose from the burning forest. ▲ **column**

com·plained
(kəm plānd´) *verb*
Said that something was unpleasant or wrong. We *complained* that the noise was too loud. ▲ **complain**

con·ceit·ed
(kən sēt´ əd) *adjective*
Having too high an opinion of oneself. The *conceited* actor couldn't believe that he wasn't chosen to star in the play.

con·ta·gious
(kən tā´ jəs) *adjective*
Easily spread from one person to another. I got sick because Judy's cold was *contagious*.

con·trac·tor
(kon´ trak tər) *noun*
A person whose job is to make sure workers and supplies are at a building site.

corn·husks
(kôrn´ husks´) *noun*
The coverings on ears of corn. ▲ **cornhusk**

cornhusk

cor·ral (kə ral´) *noun*
A fenced area that holds large animals, especially horses or cows.

crane

cranes (krānz) *noun*
Large machines used for lifting or moving heavy objects. ▲ crane

WORD STUDY

The word **crane** has more than one meaning.

- A crane is also a large wading bird. It has long legs and a long neck and bill.

- You use *crane* as a verb, too. It means to stretch your neck so that you can see over or around something.

cu·ri·ous
(kyŏŏr´ ē əs) *adjective*
Eager to learn about new or interesting things. The *curious* child asked many questions.

den·tine
(den´ tēn) *noun*
The hard, thick material that makes up most of a tooth. It is inside the tooth.

de·sign (di zīn´) *verb*
To draw something that could be built or made. Did you *design* the patterns on this rug?

dough (dō) *noun*
A mixture of flour, milk or water, and other ingredients that is made into bread or pastry.

drought (drout) *noun*
A long period of very dry weather.

dy·ers (dī´ ərz) *noun*
Workers who change the color of fabric by soaking it in dye. ▲ dyer

em·bers
(em´ bərz) *noun*
Small pieces of burned wood that are still hot and glowing in the ashes of a fire. ▲ ember

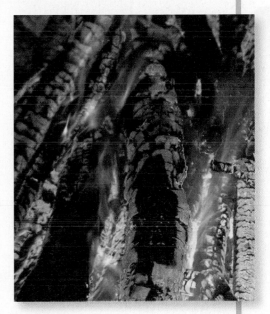
embers

a	add	o͝o	took	ə =
ā	ace	o͞o	pool	a in *above*
â	care	u	up	e in *sicken*
ä	palm	û	burn	i in *possible*
e	end	yo͞o	fuse	o in *melon*
ē	equal	oi	oil	u in *circus*
i	it	ou	pout	
ī	ice	ng	ring	
o	odd	th	thin	
ō	open	ŧh	this	
ô	order	zh	vision	

en·gi·neer
(en´ jə nēr´) *noun*
A person who is trained to design and build machines, roads, bridges, buildings, and other structures.

e·quip·ment
(i kwip´ mənt) *noun*
The tools, machines, or supplies needed for a job or activity. My fishing *equipment* includes a rod, hooks, and bait.

ex·per·i·ment
(ik sper´ ə ment´) *verb*
To try out or test an idea to prove something. The inventor wanted to *experiment* with electricity.

ex·trac·tor
(ik strak´ tər) *noun*
A machine that pulls something out with great force. We used an *extractor* to take the water out of the wet rug.

fire·storm
(fir´ stôrm´) *noun*
A giant fire that moves very quickly—like a storm. Firestorms are often pushed by strong winds.

fos·sils
(fos´ əlz) *noun*
The hardened remains of plants or animals that lived a long time ago. Dinosaur bones found in the earth are *fossils*. ▲ fossil

---

FACT FILE

- Scientists who study **fossils** are called paleontologists.

- The oldest known fossils are more than 2 billion years old.

- One of the biggest fossil bones ever discovered came from a huge dinosaur. The bone was over six feet long, and was dug up in Colorado in 1972.

---

frame·work
(frām´ wûrk´) *noun*
The part of a building or structure that gives it shape or holds it up.

gasped (gaspt) *verb*
Took in a quick breath of air because of a surprise or shock. She *gasped* with surprise when she received the award. ▲ gasp

gau·chos
(gou´ chōz) *noun*
Cowhands from South America who work on the pampas. ▲ gaucho

gauze (gôz) *noun*
A light, thin cloth that is often used as a bandage.

fossil

Gila monster

Gi·la mon·sters
(hē´ lə mon´ stərz) *noun*
Large, poisonous
lizards that live in the
southwestern part of
the United States and
in Mexico.
▲ Gila monster

graz·ing
(grā´ zing) *verb*
Eating grass that is
growing. The cows
were *grazing* in the
field. ▲ graze

grum·bled
(grum´ bəld) *verb*
Complained in a
grouchy way. Our
soccer team *grumbled*
when the game was
rained out. ▲ grumble

hoists (hoists) *noun*
Machines used to raise
objects. ▲ hoist

horned toads
(hôrnd´ tōdz´) *noun*
Small lizards that have
horn-like spines on
their heads. Horned
toads are also called
horned lizards. They
live in the western
United States.
▲ horned toad

ich·thy·o·saur
(ik´ thē ə sôr´) *noun*
A giant reptile, now
extinct, with a fishlike
body and a long snout.
Ichthyosaurs lived
millions of years ago
in the oceans.

WORD HISTORY

The word **ichthyosaur**
comes from two Greek
words, which together
mean "fish lizard."
The ichthyosaur was
a kind of dinosaur
that lived in water,
like a fish.

i·de·a (ī dē´ ə) *noun*
A thought or plan you
form in your mind.
Getting a paper route
to earn money was
Juan's *idea*.

a	add	o͝o	took	ə =
ā	ace	o͞o	pool	a in *above*
â	care	u	up	e in *sicken*
ä	palm	û	burn	i in *possible*
e	end	yo͞o	fuse	o in *melon*
ē	equal	oi	oil	u in *circus*
i	it	ou	pout	
ī	ice	ng	ring	
o	odd	th	thin	
ō	open	ᵺ	this	
ô	order	zh	vision	

horned toad

im·age (im´ ij) *noun*
Something that is seen in a mirror or a picture.

in·flam·ma·tion (in´ flə mā´ shən) *noun*
A swollen area in some part of the body that is hot, red, and sore. The splinter in her finger caused an *inflammation*.

in·for·ma·tion (in´ fər mā´ shən) *noun*
Facts and knowledge. This book has lots of *information* about monkeys.

knead·ed (nē´ did) *verb*
Mixed clay or dough with the hands by pressing and squeezing it over and over. The baker *kneaded* the bread dough for five minutes.
▲ **knead**

knead

knowl·edge (nol´ ij) *noun*
The things a person knows; information about a particular subject. Your *knowledge* of travel will help me plan my trip.

WORD HISTORY

It's no big surprise that both scientists and inventors work in laboratories! The word **laboratory** comes from the Latin word for "labor." *Labor* means the same thing as *work*.

lab·o·ra·to·ry (lab´ rə tôr´ ē) *noun*
A room or place with equipment used to do scientific experiments. The scientist looked at plant cells under the microscope in his *laboratory*.
▲ **laboratories**

Thesaurus
large
huge
giant
gigantic
enormous

large (lärj) *adjective*
Very big.

las·so (las´ ō or la soo´) *noun*
A long rope with a loop at the end used to catch cattle or horses.
▲ **lassos** or **lassoes**

lasso

light·ning

(līt´ ning) *noun*
A sudden flash of light in the sky when electricity moves between clouds or between clouds and the ground.

loom (lo͞om) *noun*

A machine for weaving thread or yarn into cloth.

manes (mānz) *noun*

The long thick hair that grows on the heads and necks of horses.
▲ mane

ma·sa (mä´ sä) *noun*

A Spanish word for a dough made of corn flour, shortening, and water. It is used to make tamales.

mu·ti·ny

(myo͞o´ tə nē) *noun*
A revolt or fight against the way things are.

op·ti·cal il·lu·sions

(op´ ti kəl i lo͞o´ zhənz)
noun Pictures that fool the eye by making something look different than how it really is.
▲ optical illusion

orchid

or·chid (ôr´ kid)

noun A plant with colorful flowers that grows in warm, damp places.

loom

a	add	o͝o	took	ə =
ā	ace	o͞o	pool	a in *above*
â	care	u	up	e in *sicken*
ä	palm	û	burn	i in *possible*
e	end	yo͞o	fuse	o in *melon*
ē	equal	oi	oil	u in *circus*
i	it	ou	pout	
ī	ice	ng	ring	
o	odd	th	thin	
ō	open	ᵺ	this	
ô	order	zh	vision	

pam·pas (pam´ pəz) *noun* A Spanish word for large plains with lots of grass and few trees. Pampas are found in South America, especially in Argentina. We rode our horses across the *pampas*.

pa·tience (pā´ shəns) *noun* The ability to work quietly and steadily without getting upset or giving up. Alex had the *patience* to put a jigsaw puzzle together.

perked (pûrkt) *verb* Became more cheerful. The sick boy *perked* up after he watched the funny cartoon. ▲ perk

plas·ter (plas´ tər) *noun* A soft, sticky mixture of lime, sand, and water that hardens as it dries. Plaster is often used to cover walls.

pos·si·bil·i·ties (pos´ ə bil´ i tēz) *noun* Things that might happen or might be true. The two *possibilities* for our vacation are the beach and the woods. ▲ possibility

pre·scrip·tion (pri skrip´ shən) *noun* A medical doctor's written order for medicine. Dr. Jenkins wrote a *prescription* for cough syrup to help me get well.

prove (pro͞ov) *verb* To show that something is true. Can you *prove* that your answer is correct?

re·vers·es (ri vûr´ siz) *verb* Turns a thing backwards, upside down, or inside out. When I push the red button, the toy car *reverses* and goes backward. ▲ reverse

scal·lion (skal´ yən) *noun* Any onion that doesn't have a large bulb; a green onion.

scallions

The word **scold** comes from an old Norse word that meant "poet." Long ago, Norse poets wrote poems that told people about the wrong things they had done. Over time, the meaning of scold changed. Now it means "to speak in an angry way."

scold·ed (skōld´ əd) *verb* Told someone in an angry way that he or she has done something wrong. Mom *scolded* the dog for tracking mud into the kitchen. ▲ scold

scratch·y (skrach´ ē) *adjective* Rough or harsh sounding. Grandpa's voice sounds *scratchy* because he has a bad cold.

sea·shells (sē´ shelz´) *noun* Shells of sea animals, such as clams or oysters. ▲ seashell

sense (sens) *noun* Good judgment. I have the good *sense* to look both ways before I cross a street.

ses·a·me noo·dles (ses´ ə mē nōōd´ lz) *noun* Flat, thin strips of dough covered with a sauce made from sesame seeds. ▲ sesame noodle

skel·e·tons (skel´ i tnz) *noun* All the bones of human or animal bodies as they fit together. ▲ skeleton

skills (skilz) *noun* Abilities to do things. I practice my swimming *skills* in the pool and at the beach. ▲ skill

seashells

smoke (smōk) *noun* The gas and tiny bits of matter that are given off when something burns. The *smoke* from our campfire made me cough.

so·lu·tion (sə lōō´ shən) *noun* The answer to a problem. Dad found a *solution* to the puzzle.

soy sauce (soi´ sôs´) *noun* A dark, salty liquid made from soybeans. It is used as a flavoring in some Asian foods.

a	add	ŏŏ	took	ə =
ā	ace	ōō	pool	a in *above*
â	care	u	up	e in *sicken*
ä	palm	û	burn	i in *possible*
e	end	yōō	fuse	o in *melon*
ē	equal	oi	oil	u in *circus*
i	it	ou	pout	
ī	ice	ng	ring	
o	odd	th	thin	
ō	open	ṯh	this	
ô	order	zh	vision	

spin·ning

(spin´ ing) *verb*
Making long, thin pieces of fiber into yarn or thread. The worker is *spinning* thread from wool. ▲ spin

spoon·ful

(spoon´ fool) *noun*
The amount that a spoon will hold.
▲ spoonfuls

spoonful

spurs (spûrz) *noun*
Pointed metal pieces worn on the heels of boots that are used to poke a horse to make it move forward. ▲ spur

stam·pedes

(stam pēdz´) *noun*
Herds of animals moving wildly in one direction because something has frightened them.
▲ stampede

steth·o·scope

(steth´ ə skōp) *noun*
An instrument used by doctors to listen to a person's heartbeat or breathing.

WORD HISTORY

Stethoscope comes from two Greek words meaning "chest" and "examine." Today doctors often use stethoscopes to listen to, or examine, people's chests.

su·per·struc·ture

(soo´ pər struk´ chər) *noun* The part of a building that rises above the basement.

ta·ma·les

(tə mä´ lēz) *noun*
Mexican food made of chopped meat and red peppers in a cornmeal dough. The mixture is wrapped in corn husks and then cooked.
▲ tamale

stethoscope

thought (thôt) *verb*
Used your mind to create ideas or make decisions. I *thought* of some questions to ask the author.

tooth·aches

(tooth´ āks´) *noun*
Pains in or near teeth.
▲ toothache

tamales

vol·ca·noes

(vol kā´ nōz) *noun*
Openings in the earth's
surface through which
rock, gas, and steam
erupt. ▲ volcano

volcano

FACT FILE

- There are more than
  800 active **volcanoes**
  in the world.

- The hot melted rock
  that flows out of
  erupting **volcanoes** is
  called lava.

- **Volcanoes** exist in
  the oceans as well
  as on land.

weav·ers

(wē´ vərz) *noun*
Workers who make
cloth or rugs on a loom
by passing threads or
yarn over and under
in a crisscross pattern.
▲ weaver

wheel·chair

(hwēl´ châr or wēl´ châr)
noun A chair on wheels
that a sick, injured, or
disabled person uses for
moving around.

wheelchair

whis·pered

(hwis´ pərd or wis´ pərd)
verb Talked very quietly
or softly. I *whispered* a
secret to my best friend.
▲ whisper

wis·dom

(wiz´ dəm) *noun*
Knowledge, experience,
and good judgment.
The teacher has *wisdom*
because he knows a lot.

wise (wīz) *adjective*

Having or showing
intelligence or good
judgment. The *wise*
woman knew a way to
solve the problem.

yank (yangk) *verb*

To give a sudden, strong
pull. My dog can *yank*
the leash out of my
hands when she's excited.

a	add	o͞o	took	ə =	
ā	ace	o͞o	pool	a in *above*	
â	care	u	up	e in *sicken*	
ä	palm	û	burn	i in *possible*	
e	end	yo͞o	fuse	o in *melon*	
ē	equal	oi	oil	u in *circus*	
i	it	ou	pout		
ī	ice	ng	ring		
o	odd	th	thin		
ō	open	ᵵh	this		
ô	order	zh	vision		

Acknowledgments

Grateful acknowledgment is made to the following sources for permission to reprint from previously published material. The publisher has made diligent efforts to trace the ownership of all copyrighted material in this volume and believes that all necessary permissions have been secured. If any errors or omissions have inadvertently been made, proper corrections will gladly be made in future editions.

Cover, Unit Opener, and Unit 3 *On the Job* Table of Contents: from DOCTOR DESOTO by William Steig. Copyright © 1982 by William Steig. Reprinted by permission of Farrar, Straus & Giroux, Inc.

Unit 1 *What's New* Table of Contents: From RAMONA FOREVER by Beverly Cleary, illustrations by Alan Tiegreen. Copyright © 1984 by Beverly Cleary. Reprinted by permission of Morrow Junior Books, a division of William Morrow & Company, Inc.

Unit 2 *Big Plans*: From UP GOES THE SKYSCRAPER! by Gail Gibbons. Copyright © 1986 by Gail Gibbons. Reprinted with permission of Atheneum Books for Young Readers, Simon & Schuster Children's Publishing Division.

Unit 1 *What's New*: "Gila Monsters Meet You at the Airport" from GILA MONSTERS MEET YOU AT THE AIRPORT. Text copyright © 1980 by Marjorie Weinman Sharmat. Illustrations copyright © 1980 by Byron Barton. Reprinted by permission of Simon & Schuster Books for Young Readers, Simon & Schuster Children's Publishing Division.

"Gila Monster March" and "Alligator Stomp" from THE REPTILE BALL by Jacqueline K. Ogburn. Copyright © 1997 by Jacqueline K. Ogburn. Used by permission of Dial Books for Young Readers, a division of Penguin Putnam Inc.

"Another Big Event" from RAMONA FOREVER by Beverly Cleary. Copyright © 1984 by Beverly Cleary. Reprinted by permission of Morrow Junior Books, a division of William Morrow & Company, Inc.

"I Am" from IT'S RAINING LAUGHTER by Nikki Grimes, photographs by Myles Pinkney. Text copyright © 1997 by Nikki Grimes. Photographs copyright © 1997 by Myles Pinkney. Used by permission of Dial Books for Young Readers, a division of Penguin Putnam Inc.

"How My Family Lives in America" from HOW MY FAMILY LIVES IN AMERICA by Susan Kuklin. Copyright © 1992 by Susan Kuklin. Reprinted with permission of Simon & Schuster Books for Young Readers, Simon & Schuster Children's Publishing Division.

"Kids Speak Up to Save Native Languages" by Sarah Jane Brian from SCHOLASTIC NEWS, November 12, 1993. Copyright © 1993 by Scholastic Inc. Reprinted by permission.

"On the Pampas" from ON THE PAMPAS by Maria Cristina Brusca. Copyright © 1991 by Maria Cristina Brusca. Reprinted by arrangement with Henry Holt and Co.

"How the World Got Wisdom" from THE ADVENTURES OF SPIDER: WEST AFRICAN FOLK TALES. Text copyright © 1964 by Joyce Cooper Arkhurst. Illustrations copyright © 1964 by Barker/Black Studios Inc. Reprinted by permission of Little, Brown and Company.

"Parent to Child" was originally published as "Black Parent to Child" from ALL BEAUTIFUL THINGS. Copyright © 1983 by Naomi F. Faust. Published by Lotus Press, Detroit, Michigan, distributed by Michigan State University Press. Reprinted by permission of the author.

Unit 2 *Big Plans*: "The Little Red Ant and the Great Big Crumb" from THE LITTLE RED ANT AND THE GREAT BIG CRUMB. Text copyright © 1995 by Shirley Climo. Illustrations copyright © 1995 by Francisco X. Mora. Reprinted by permission of Clarion Books/Houghton Mifflin Company. All rights reserved.

"Who Pulled the Plug in My Ant Farm?" from SOMETHING BIG HAS BEEN HERE by Jack Prelutsky. Text copyright © 1990 by Jack Prelutsky. Illustrations copyright © by James Stevenson. By permission of Greenwillow Books, a division of William Morrow & Company, Inc.

"The Book of Think" from THE BOOK OF THINK by Marilyn Burns. Copyright © 1976 by Marilyn Burns. By permission of Little, Brown and Company.

"A Drink for Crow" and "Crossing the River" from STORIES TO SOLVE: FOLKTALES FROM AROUND THE WORLD by George Shannon, illustrated by Peter Sis. Text copyright © 1985 by George W.B. Shannon. Illustrations copyright © 1985 by Peter Sis. Reprinted by permission of Greenwillow Books, a division of William Morrow & Company, Inc.

"Dragon in the Rocks" from DRAGON IN THE ROCKS by Marie Day. Copyright © 1991 by Marie Day. Reprinted with permission of the publisher, Greey de Pencier Books.

"The Steam Shovel" by Rowena Bennett, from STORY-TELLER POEMS. Copyright © 1948 by Rowena Bennett, copyright renewed © 1976. Reprinted by permission of Kenneth C. Bennett, Literary Executor of the Estate of Rowena Bennett. Illustration by Arnold Lobel from SING A SONG OF POPCORN selected by Beatrice Schenk de Regniers et. al. Illustration copyright © 1988 by Arnold Lobel. Reprinted by permission of Scholastic Inc.

"Up Goes the Skyscraper!" from UP GOES THE SKYSCRAPER! by Gail Gibbons. Copyright © 1986 by Gail Gibbons. Reprinted with permission of Atheneum Books for Young Readers, Simon & Schuster Children's Publishing Division.

Architectural sketch used by permission of Loebl, Schlossman & Hackl, Chicago, IL.

"A Picture Book of Thomas Alva Edison" from A PICTURE BOOK OF THOMAS ALVA EDISON by David A. Adler. Text copyright © 1996 by David A. Adler. Illustrations copyright © 1996 by John and Alexandra Wallner. All rights reserved. Reprinted by permission of Holiday House, Inc.

Text and diagram from WHAT'S THE SCOOP? by Maura McCasted. Logo and forms from Invent America, United States Patent Model Foundation, 1505 Powhatan Street, Alexandria, VA 22314.

Unit 3 *On the Job*: "The Story of Z" from THE STORY OF Z by Jean Modesitt, illustrations by Lonni Sue Johnson. Text copyright © 1990 Jeanne Modesitt. Illustrations copyright © 1990 Lonni Sue Johnson. Reprinted with permission of Simon and Schuster Books for Young Readers, Simon & Schuster Children's Publishing Division.

"The Bug Zoo" poster is used by the kind permission of the Liberty Science Center, Jersey City, NJ.

"Too Many Tamales" from TOO MANY TAMALES by Gary Soto, illustrations by Ed Martinez. Text copyright © 1993 by Gary Soto. Illustrations copyright © 1993 by Ed Martinez. Used by permission of G.P. Putnam's Sons, a division of Penguin Putnam Inc.

"Ode to Corn" from LAUGHING TOMATOES AND OTHER SPRING POEMS by Francisco X. Alarcón, illustrations by Maya Christina Gonzalez. Poems copyright © 1997 by Francisco X. Alarcón. Pictures copyright © 1997 by Maya Christina Gonzalez. Reprinted by permission of Children's Book Press.

"Fire! In Yellowstone" from FIRE! IN YELLOWSTONE by Robert Ekey. Text copyright © 1990 by Falcon Publishing Co., Inc. Format copyright © 1990 by Gareth Stevens, Inc. Text and photos first published in book form by Gareth Stevens, Inc. Milwaukee, WI, under the title "Fire! in Yellowstone." Text used by permission of Gareth Stevens, Inc.

"Smoke Jumper" from *National Geographic World*, August 1994. Reprinted with permission of *National Geographic World*.

"Fire Fighter Raps It Up!" by Johnny Ruiz, from SCHOLASTIC NEWS, October 1992. Copyright © 1992 by Johnny Ruiz. Reprinted by permission of Louis M. Atlas.

"The Legend of the Persian Carpet" from THE LEGEND OF THE PERSIAN CARPET by Tomie dePaola, illustrated by Claire Ewart. Text copyright © 1993 by Tomie dePaola. Illustrations copyright © 1993 by Claire Ewart. Used by permission of G.P. Putnam's Sons, a division of Penguin Putnam Inc.

"Disney" signature logo, illustrations, and photos for "High Tech Carpet" copyright © Disney Enterprises, Inc.

"Doctor De Soto" from DOCTOR DE SOTO by William Steig. Copyright © 1982 by William Steig. Reprinted by permission of Farrar, Straus & Giroux, Inc.